U0124073

International
Style Restaurants

國際風格餐廳

國家圖書館出版品預行編目資料

國際風格餐廳＝International style restaurants／吳宗敏主編.
初版. 臺中市：棠雍圖書. 2007.12
面：公分
ISBN 978-986-82778-7-8 (精裝)
1.餐廳 2.商店設計
483.8
96018990

Copyright® 2008 by TANG YUNG

TANG YUNG Co.,Ltd.
Publisher: Danny Chao
Add: No.146, Wucyuan 1st st, West District, Taichung City 403, Taiwan (R.O.C.) TEL: 886-4-23750087
FAX: 886-4-23750363 E-mail: dannychao@tybook.tw http://www.tybook.tw

Date of Publish January,2008

Printed in Hong Kong

著作權所有
不得侵害。未經書商同意不得以任何方式使用或複製本書任何內容。但報章評論或論文得簡短引用內文。如需資料請洽廣州市
唐藝文化傳播有限公司

棠雍圖書有限公司
發行人/趙立雍
地址/臺中市西區五權一街146號
電話/886-4-23750087 傳眞/886-4-23750363
E-mail:dannychao@tybook.tw
http://www.tybook.tw

初版日期/2008年元月(第一刷)

印刷/香港

ISBN 978-986-82778-7-8

CONTENTS 目录

PREAMBLE

The Spring of Restaurant Design

There is a folksay of "food is what matters to the people"; Gaozi, Chinese ancient virtuous and sagacious talent, once said, to enjoy food and beauty is man's nature, so, it is one of human's nature to eat and drink. Restaurant space, which is based on the culture of eating and drinking, is not only a representation space, but also a special cultural carrier.

At present, restaurants of various scales and styles spring up like mushrooms in the cities we live in, the investment of restaurant in China has entered into a stage of tillage like spring. Since the reform and opening begin, today people's concept of eating is no longer the functional demand of simply maintaining the lives in that poor age, but has evolved into a kind of living attitude of people in the city, and a kind of expression of developing condition of the city culture. For the designer of the restaurant, modern concept of "restaurant" has been not only the decorating standard and function requirement, but also an expression of social philosophic thought, ideology, culture and history factors, concept of management, the embodiment of the cultural improvement, which combines "dish style" with "subject matter" to form a synthesis of brand, that is unification of form and content.

"Space" in Ci Hai (a Chinese word dictionary) is interpreted as "a form of material existent, expression of extensive and stretchy material existence". For space design, function composition, interface compartmentation and configuration, color, material technique are limited space concept, while for cultural layer of the space and topic concept, they are limitless concept. These limitless "culture" and "theme" space influences the management orientation, brand figure, cultural content and design style directly, different themes give customers different eating enjoyment: the romantic sentiment of western-style food, the fervency and riot of Sichuan Cuisine, and Hunan Cuisine, the lofty and generous Dongbei Cuisine, the insipidity and elegance of Guangdong Cuisine, the noble and exquisite Chaoshan Cuisine… Different dishes form different cultural carriers, different cultural and historical tone and different topic requirement they not only provide better imagining space, but also raise newer researching topics.

Design usually have some scheming factors, design and scheme connect to each other, influence each other, promote each other and substitute each other, existing together. Scheme is a process of the design of cultural notion blending with management and promotion, while design is to increase additional value after blending cultural and historical factors as well as scheme factors, to sublime design during scheming.

I am honored at engaging in design education and design practice for nearly twenty years, during the design of one restaurant space after another, I feel that the design of restaurant is not only a design of restaurant, but also has sublimed into an art expression of a cultural space. Design becomes a kind of humanized solicitude to the restaurant management from former function satisfaction. Topic space cannot be designed as designers' wish, but should on the basis of requirement of management orientation and cost performance of investment, it is not so easy to design a restaurant under the various restrictions with harmonious management and topic, and at the same time satisfy the owner and attract customers.

The design of restaurant is not only for space, but also should blend the design into management. The process of design is also a process of scheme, which i absolutely to raise more challenge to designers. Of course, it is not so easy for everybody to achieve it. It needs solid professional knowledge of art design and the exploring experiences to restaurant management. No matter in restaurant design or any other kinds of design, designers should base on management factors and cultural and historical factors to extract rich nourishment in managing and scheming in cultural and historical environment. Besides, designers also should have high social responsibility and unique market insight, thinking while combining design concept and managing scheme. If only all of these are achieved, more economic benefit would be achieved.

There is a profound eating cultural tradition in Chinese, with long history of eating space. After thousands of years of historical sedimentation, especially with high-speed development of material products today, numerous excellent works on the design of restaurant have emerged in the wave of social economy with so many things to see and make people relaxed and happy. The book integrates many classical cases of restaurant, involving in Chinese style, southeast Asian style, European style, modern fashion style and Japanese style and so on. All those have absolutely brought good chance to learn and communicate for domestic eating enterprises and designers, and also bring the breath of spring for design, scheme and operation of eating area. Who say that "fashion" and "classic" are always opposite to each other? In the Zuim fashion restaurant in Ningbo, the fashion and classic realize perfect mixture just like water and fish do, which makes people enjoy eating there . Just like narration from Tian Xia Yi Jia, "The person who wants to possess the most excellent thing in the world should first get its soul and then its essence". The key of the success of restaurant design also should be put in "heart" and "ideal".

It is sure that when I was enjoying those works, it is also the new design concept and unique design tact, as well as the precise working attitude and perfecti study thought which make me want to be the editor in chief of this book seems that this book brings spring wind into design area, while breathing the fresh air, our design thoughts fly freely in the breath of spring.

Wu Zongmin
July 10, 2007

6

餐厅设计的春天

俗话说："民以食为天"；中国古代的贤哲告子曾说过："食、色，性也"，意指餐饮是人类的本性之一。餐饮是一种文化，而以此文化为基础的餐饮空间，不仅是一种单纯的空间表现，更是一种特殊文化的载体。

当前，各种规模和各种类型的餐厅在都市中如雨后春笋般迅猛发展，我国餐厅的投资建设进入了一个春天般的耕耘建设阶段。改革开放发展到今天，人们对"吃"的概念已经不再是那贫穷的年代里维持生命的简单需要，它已经演变成为都市人的一种生活态度，是一个城市文明发展程度的表现。对于餐厅的设计者来说，现代的"餐厅"概念已经不仅仅是装饰和功能，而是一个对社会的哲学思想、意识形态、人文因素、经营理念的表达，是文明进步的体现，是将"菜式"和"主题"结合起来，形成一个品牌的综合体，也就是形式和内容的统一。

"空间"一词在辞海中解释为"物质存在的一种形式，是物质存在的广延性和伸张性的表现"。对空间设计而言，功能布局、界面分隔以及形态、色彩、材料、技术等是有限的空间概念，对空间的文化层面以及主题概念而言，则是无限的空间概念。无限的"文化"和"主题"空间直接影响到餐厅的经营定位、品牌形象、文化内容以及设计风格，不同的"主题"给予消费者不同的用餐享受——西餐的浪漫情调；川、湘菜的热烈奔放；东北菜的豪情大方；粤菜的清淡高雅；潮汕风味的尊贵细致……不同的菜式形成不同的文化载体、不同的人文气息、不同的主题，既给设计师提供了更多的想像空间，同时也给设计师提出了更新的研究课题。

设计始终具有一定的策划因素，设计与策划是互相联系、互相影响、互相促进并共同存在的。策划是把文化概念的设计融入经营管理，营销策划的过程，设计是在融入人文因素和策划因素后，增加设计的附加值，使设计在策划中得到升华。

本人有幸从事设计实践和设计教育近20年，在一个又一个餐饮空间的设计过程中，感觉到餐饮空间的设计已经不仅仅只是一个餐饮空间的设计，而是上升到了一个文化空间的艺术表现，设计从过去对功能的满足上升到了对餐厅经营策略以及对人文精神的关怀。主题空间并不能任由

设计者为所欲为，而要建立在经营定位、投资的性价比等基础上，在各种条条框框的约束下，设计出一个经营与主题相协调，既让业主满意，又对消费者有吸引力的餐厅，并不是一件容易的事情。

餐饮空间的设计不仅仅是为空间而设计，更应该把设计融入到经营中去，设计的过程也就是策划的过程，这向设计者提出了更大的挑战。当然，不是所有的设计师都能做到这一点，这需要扎实的艺术设计专业知识，对餐厅经营的多元探索经验。无论是餐厅设计或是其他的门类设计，都是以经营因素和人文因素为基础的，要从经营策划和人文环境中吸取丰富的营养。不仅如此，设计师还要具有高度的社会责任感和与众不同的市场洞察力，并能将设计理念与经营策划结合在一起思考，这样才能为设计项目带来更大的经济效益。

我国有着深厚的餐饮文化传统，餐饮空间的历史十分悠久。经过千百年的历史沉淀，特别是到了物质高度发展的今天，餐饮空间设计在社会经济的浪潮中涌现出无数优秀的作品，这些作品令人目不暇接，让人心旷神怡。《国际风格餐厅》一书，集合了许多经典的餐饮空间的案例，涉及到中式风格、东南亚风格、欧式风格、现代风格、日式风格等，无疑为国内餐饮企业和设计师带来了极好的学习和交流的机会，同时也为餐饮业的设计策划和运作模式带来了春天的气息。谁说"时尚"和"古典"是永久的对立者？在宁波醉美时尚餐厅里，时尚和古典实现了"鱼"与"水"般的相融，让来此享受的人们既得"鱼"、又得"水"。正如天地一家所表述的"欲得天下者，必先得其心，必先得其志"，餐饮空间设计的成功，亦以得其"心"、"志"为关键。

当然，让我有做本书主编的冲动的还有这些作品新颖的创作理念和别出心裁的设计手法，以及设计师严谨的工作态度和追求完美的治学思想，这些仿佛为设计界吹来了春天的风。呼吸着这清新的空气，我们的设计思维也在春天的气息里自由地飞翔。

2007.7.10

Modern Style
现代风格

Cool and Vogue
清冷时尚

Not only the coolness, but also the warmth can become the vogue expression in dining spaces.

无论酷酷的清冷，还是柔和的暖意，都能成为餐饮空间时尚的表情。

Title: Hua Ze Xuan
Designer: Wang Kun
Design company: Shenzhen Yiding Decoration and Design Co., Ltd.
Materials: Timber, Stone，Glass，Wall cloth，Stainless steel
Floor area: 1,000m²

项目名称: 花泽轩
设 计 师: 王锟
设计公司: 深圳艺鼎装饰设计有限公司
主要饰材: 木材、石材、玻璃、墙布、不锈钢
建筑面积: 1000㎡

1. Stylish and elegant VIP room
2. Dining seat arrangement depends on the spatial layout
3. A VIP room partitioned by the glass walls
4. Lobby full of vigor and elegance

1．时尚而不失高雅的贵宾房
2．相对排列的餐位布局由空间的形状决定
3．玻璃墙体隔离出来的贵宾房
4．奔放而雅致的休息区

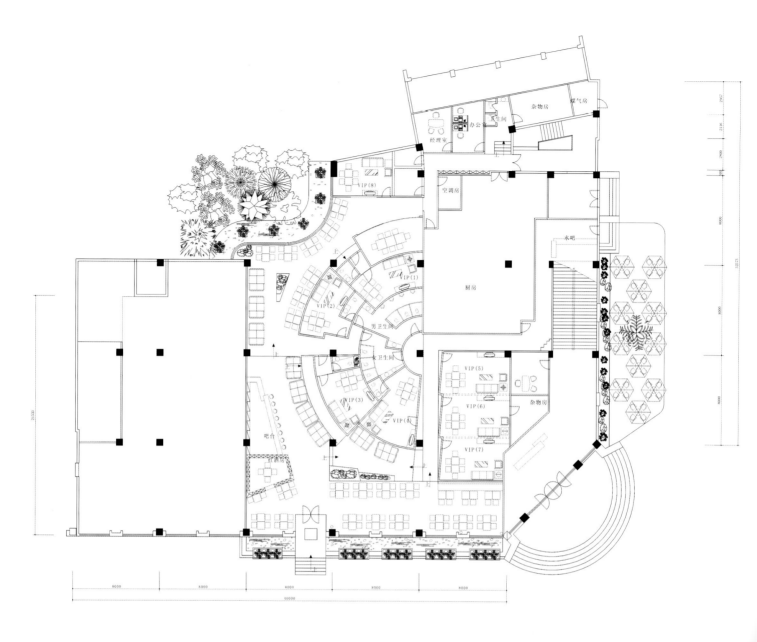

Design Concept:

The designer of this project has his original sight and pursue of fashion. And accordingly, the unconventional effect in decoration and products is the goal of any design project. There are a lot of modern and compact designing techniques, which thereby easily weaken the design effect and make the space dull and featureless without rich content.

However, Hua Ze Xuan is indeed a very viable and successful case of simplicity. It adopts a series of commonplace decoration materials such as timber, stone, glass and stainless steel to enrich the space. Although giving a sense of coolness, these materials plus some flower patterns add a touch of elegance and vigor in the space. The red sofas and seats in the cool ambience animate the space like flame and warm the atmosphere in a flash. In addition, the casually scattered natural ornaments at the corners and near the wall also evoke the unsophisticated effect in the space.

The simple stone flooring, neat and unornamented walls together create an elegant, peaceful and relaxed dining ambience in this modern restaurant.

1. Arrangement plan
2. Several wild flowers add the natural refinement into the space
3. The arrangement of dining seats and the bar design have consistent style
4. Suitable performance of light and shade of lighting in the restaurant

1．平面布置图
2．几朵野花让空间充满自然的雅致
3．餐位的布置与吧台设计风格统一
4．餐厅灯光的明暗处理恰到好处

设计说明：

本案的设计师对时尚有独到的见解与追求。在装修及摆设方面取得与众不同的效果是任何一个设计作品所追求的目标。现代简约设计的方式有很多，但是走简约路线容易发生偏离，使空间显得单薄，不够饱满。

泽轩则是一个将简约路线走得很沉稳也很成功的案例。它借用一些再普通不过的饰材，如木材、石材、玻璃、不锈钢等，将空间构架出来。这些材质让空间给人以清冷的感觉，加上一些小花的点缀，让空间多了一丝高雅与活力。红色沙发和坐椅的设计则是清冷氛围中的一丝火焰，将热情点燃，让气氛在瞬间热烈起来。不经意地陈列在角落、墙边的自然饰物，给空间带来一些淳朴。

实的石材地面，整齐、不加装饰的墙面，强烈的色彩对比，让这个现代餐饮空间呈现高雅、平静、逸的就餐氛围。

1	
2	3
	4 5

1. The stable curved wall functions as the main wall in the VIP room
2. Lights with diversified designs indicate different functional areas
3. A set of red desks and sofas endows the space with nobleness and passion
4. The seats near the window enable people to enjoy more unhindered views
5. The concise surface sets off the main spatial part better

1．稳重的弧形墙体作为贵宾房的主要背景墙
2．不同的灯光设计突出了不同区域的功能
3．成套的红色座椅与沙发使空间洋溢着高贵与热情
4．临窗布置的餐位能获得更为开阔的视野
5．简洁的界面更好地划分了空间

1. Restaurant aisle
2. The rough walls show a natural form in this space
3. The washroom purposely has rough treatment on the walls

1．餐厅走道
2．粗糙的墙面让空间呈现自然的形态
3．洗手间刻意做了粗糙处理的墙面

Variety
形形色色

The restaurant in the digital epoch adopts "shape" and "color" with the simplest designing vocabulary, which gives the most precise and complete definitions of "vogue" and "fashion".

数码时代的餐厅，借用"形"与"色"，用最简略的"语言"，给"前卫"与"时尚"做了最准确、最全面的诠释。

Title: New Century Beilun Commerce Bar
Designer: Wang Jiming
Design company: Ningbo New Century Decoration and
Design Co.，Ltd.
Materials: Wood，Marble，Glass
Floor area: 200m²

项目名称: 新世纪北仑商务吧
设 计 师: 王寄明
设计公司: 宁波新世纪装饰设计有限公司
主要饰材: 木材、大理石、玻璃
建筑面积: 200m²

	2	
1		3

1. Window blind with different colors
2. Multicolored effects achieve the charm in the interior space
3. The stone wine cabinet is very stable

1．五颜六色的百叶窗
2．室内空间的诱惑力来自于五彩缤纷的色彩
3．石材打造的特色酒柜给人以厚重感

Design Concept:

Shape and color are two basic and crucial factors for the interior design. Through the different treatments and process of shape and color, the designer creates colorful cases in all kinds of forms for the interior space.

This case is a commerce bar in the style of Bop Art, that is to say, the designer devotes himself to a product with the treatment of spatial shape and color.

The designer starts from the shape of the space, and in order to break the mechanical feeling which the rectangle plane produces, a lot of oblique lines of 45 degrees are adopted. The alternation of all sorts of oblique lines, whether from the strip ceiling to the seat or from the ground to the reflection wall, makes each layer full of modern feeling and penetrating power. The bar counter is the focal point of the commerce bar, therefore, the designer on purposely uses the incline style to draw people's eyes to the center just from the entrance hall, and the corresponding models on top to echo with it simultaneously. The table board uses the bar code design, which enables it to have a kind of vanguard and dynamic feeling in digital times.

Shape is just a basic frame built in the space, and only the injection of corresponding elements and colors can make everything unified organically to become a space with life and spirit. In the choice of material, the designer pays great attention to the color match, from the simple matte black slate round to the black galaxy reflection wall that passes the mysterious feeling etc, which makes the commerce massive and pragmatic. However, if the utilization and processing of "color" just stop like this, it will be very difficult for this spatial design to come out from the common interior design. Here, many big French windows endow the space with more room to be used. When the simple shutters present the order of shallow orange, light yellow, pink green, light blue and lavender, the commerce bar, like an angel who owns beautiful wings, enchants everyone.

When lights are lit, wandering around the gorgeous and enchanting commerce bar, you will feel the indoor space, with the combination of shape and color, sending out attractive charm, walking into it, watching the splendid shape and color stretch in the space, and hugging a colorful night.

1\2. The lines are very clear and neat to outline the space
3. Light and color are the only decorations in the space
1 \ 2 . 空间的线条明朗，轮廓鲜明
3 . 光与色是空间惟一的装饰

1	2	3	4
		5	

1. A wealth of diagonal lines adds mysterious feeling in the devious space
2. Bar of restaurant
3. The arrangement of droplights can suggest the layout of bar
4. Spatial detail-sculpture
5. Arrangement plan

1．大量斜线条的运用让空间曲折迂回，具有神秘感
2．餐厅的吧台
3．根据吊灯的排列不难判断出吧台的形态
4．空间细部——雕塑艺术
5．平面布置图

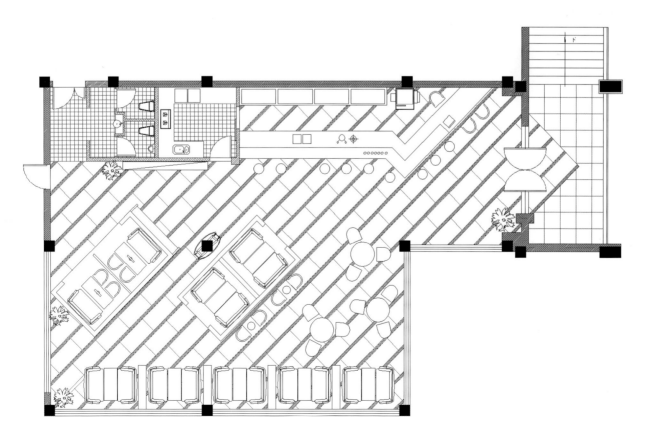

1. This red-and-white round droplight is concise and modern
2. The incomplete partition doesn't show closed effect in this private room
3. The seating near window is neat and ordered

1．红白相配的圆形吊灯简约而时尚
2．不完全的隔断让雅座空间消除封闭感
3．餐位沿窗整齐排列

设计说明：

形与色为室内设计的两大基本而关键的要素。设计师们通过对形与色的把握和处理，为室内空间设计出了形形色色、多姿多彩的方案。

本案为一个带有波普艺术风格的商务吧，同时也是设计师致力于空间形色处理的产物。

设计师从空间的"形"入手，为打破矩形平面产生的呆板感，导入了多组45°的斜线，无论从条形天花板到座位，还是从地面到反射墙面，各种斜线的穿插，使各个层面富有现代感和穿透力。吧台是商务吧的焦点，因此从门厅起设计师就刻意以倾斜的方式把人们的视线引入中心，同时在塑上做相应的造型与之呼应。吧台的台面采用了条形码设计，具有数码时代的前卫感和动态感。

"形"只是设计师在空间搭建的一个基本框架，只有注入相应的元素及色彩，各个面才能有机地结合起来，形成有生命和灵性的空间。在材质的选择上，设计师也注重了色彩的搭配，从朴素的亚光黑板岩地面到透着神秘感的黑金砂反射墙面等等，整个商务吧有一个厚重务实的基调。但如果"色"的运用和处理仅止于此，这一空间的设计就很难从一般的室内设计中凸现出来。多面落地大窗的存在赋予空间更多发挥的余地，简单的百叶窗以浅橙、淡黄、粉绿、浅蓝、淡紫次递呈现时，商务吧便如长了缤纷翅膀的天使般，变得迷人起来。

华灯初上时分，倘佯在绚丽迷人的商务吧周围，形与色相融的室内空间散发着诱人的魅力，走进去，欣赏形与色的精彩在空间蔓延的同时，也拥抱一个多姿多彩的夜晚。

Yu Hu Die

玉湖蝶

What people seek for is a peaceful place nestled in the bustling downtown. Inviting sworn friends, they can enjoy the good wine and delicious food and sing. This place puts them at their ease in a warm ambience.

于喧闹的都市觅一个宁静之处，邀三五好友，美酒美食，轻谈浅唱，品的是宁静舒怀，暖的是冰心一片。

Title: Yu Hu Die Restaurant
Designer: Qian Wanpeng
Design company: Hansen Decoration and Kunpeng Design Institute
Materials: Import wallpaper，Custom-built steel framed stair，Aluminum composite panel，Gauze
Floor area: 400m²

项目名称：玉湖蝶主题餐厅
设 计 师：钱万鹏
设计公司：汉森装饰鲲鹏营造设计机构
主要饰材：进口墙纸、定制钢架楼梯、铝塑板、透纱
建筑面积：*400m²*

	2
1	3

1. Engaging effect in conciseness
2. The soft decorations on the 2nd floor are very rich and colorful
3. Panoramic view of the 1st floor restaurant

1．简约中的妖娆
2．二楼空间的软装饰更丰富多彩
3．一楼餐厅全景

Design Concept:

The design subject of this space derives from the purity and sanctity of the jade, the quietness and tolerance of the lake and the elegance and beauty of the butterfly. The name of the restaurant is so appropriate and beautiful that it can move the people sufficiently, bringing romance and goodliness to the common and real life.

According to these three themes, the designer keeps the original space intact and makes use of the structure beauty of its own to put up a translucent high stairs to the clouds, which creates a new form of the space.

As for the outdoor surface of this restaurant, the designer with no taboo uses the black color that can give people the feeling of fashion and delicacy to the upmost. That is to cover the building facade of traditional design with a layer of black shell — one traditional layer and one modern layer, plus several emerald green bamboos swaying in the wind. Some natural elements are employed to neutralize the tradition and modernity.

Since the space is designed as a room for catering and service, the embodiment of the service concept is indispensable. In this regard, the designer puts the emphasis on the design of the washroom. The wall of the washroom is covered with decorative pattern wallpapers, and the function of the dressing room is also realized in the washroom, which promotes the level of the restaurant on the whole.

A perfect restaurant definitely can not lack the elements of warmth, and the soft decoration can bring tenderness and gentle feeling to the space. In the restaurant, lavender gauze curtains hanging in many places and cotton tablecloths can give people considerate and exquisite care. The wall of warm colors and the subdued light make the atmosphere much warmer.

1/2. The lightness staircase which likes a stairway to heaven is light and transparent
3. A corner of the restaurant

1 / 2. 轻盈的楼梯如一架天梯，轻巧、透明
3. 餐厅一隅

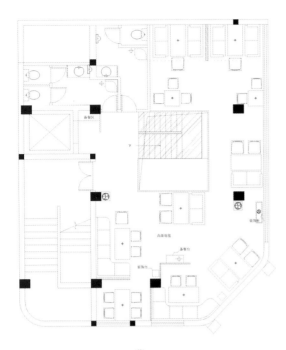

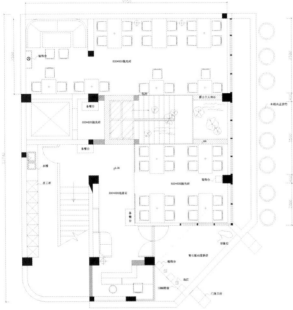

1. 2nd floor arrangement plan
2. 1st floor arrangement plan
3. The exquisite and deluxe decorations against the warm background
4. Viewed from the 2nd floor, the arrangement of seating on the 1st floor looks like an abstract painting
5. Elevation A
6. Elevation F

1．二楼平面布置图
2．一楼平面布置图
3．暖意背景下的精致与奢华
4．从二楼俯视，一楼餐位的布置犹如一幅抽象画
5．A立面
6．F立面

Simplicity is still the entire space style of the restaurant, and there are not too many sophisticated decorative patterns. The column of the mirror adopts the simplified crooked patterns and the modern material to express the Chinese subject with elegantly simple tone as the primary tone. The romantic feeling of the soft screen is extremely presented here.

The existence of water is not neglected in this design, and the arrangement of the spatial water features looks artful and appropriate. There are two circles of water area in the restaurant. One is in the middle of the hall, and the other is on the left of the entrance of the restaurant. The water can evoke vitalities, and it is also the symbol of wealth. This is a kind of Chinese traditional culture, and the design of the water features in space helps publicize the Chinese traditional culture.

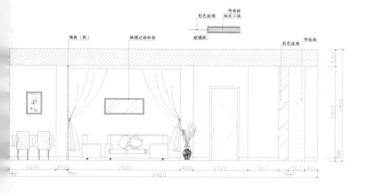

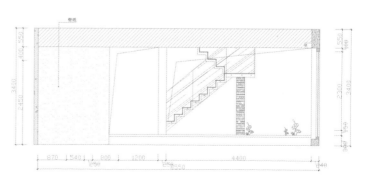

设计说明:

玉的冰清与圣洁，湖的宁静与包容，蝶的飘逸和美丽，都是这个空间的设计主题。贴切而唯美的餐厅名字，足以打动人心，给平实的生活带来一份浪漫与美好。

围绕这三个主题，设计师原封不动地保留了原来的空间，利用了它自身的结构美，架了一部半透明的天梯，直上云霄，塑造出新的空间形态。

在餐厅外立面的塑造上，为了使空间具有时尚感，设计师毫无避讳地运用了最能给人以时尚与精致感觉的黑色，即在传统设计的建筑门面上罩了一层黑色板壳。一层传统，一层现代，再加上几棵翠竹在风中摇曳，传统与现代的对立中，有了一些自然的元素进行调和。

空间既然定性为餐饮服务空间，对服务概念的体现是不可缺少的，设计师把重点定在洗手间设计上。洗手间的墙面采用花纹墙纸，并在洗手间增加了休息化妆区的功能，这就让餐厅的层次得到整体的提升。

一个完美的餐厅，一定不会缺乏温情的元素，而软装饰是最能给空间带来温情和柔和感的。餐厅内多处悬挂的淡紫纱帘、棉质的桌布，都能带给人体贴、细腻的关怀。色泽温暖的墙面，柔和的灯光，使温馨的感觉更加浓烈。

餐厅整个空间风格还是以简洁为主，没有过多复杂的装饰图案，镜面立柱采用了简化后的勾回纹，用现代材料表达中式主题，以淡雅的色调为主色调，将软隔断充满情调的特点表现到极致。

餐厅的设计没有忽略水的存在，空间水景的处理显得巧妙、得体。餐厅中有两圈水体，一圈位于大厅中央，一圈在餐厅入口的左侧。水能孕育生机，有生财的象征意味，这是一种中国传统文化。水景的设计实现了中国传统文化的宣扬。

1. The seats decorated by pure white cloth look noble and graceful
2. With emerald bamboos outside, this restaurant is just like a beautiful picture
3. The light color and elegant valance add the gracefulness into this space
4. Floor lamp is the only leading actor in this environment

1. 纯白布料包裹出的餐位更显简洁、淡雅
2. 窗外翠竹掩映，餐厅俨然掉入一幅优美的画里
3. 色彩淡雅的帷幔让空间充满万千柔情
4. 落地灯是这一空间的主角

Nature and Stylish Elements
自然＋流行元素

The famous designer Mies Van de Rohe has ever said a classical sentence – "Less is more". The ample natural and stylish elements in spaces are showed here in a simple manner.
著名设计大师米斯·凡德洛有一句经典设计名言"少即多"，空间丰富的自然与流行元素以简略的形式呈现。

Title: Lejia Fast-food Restaurant
Designer: He Yongming
Design company: He Yongming Designer Studio
Materials: Glass，Fireproofing board，Spray painting，Man-made stone
Floor area: 280m²

项目名称: 乐嘉快餐厅
设 计 师: 何永明
设计公司: 何永明设计师工作室
主要饰材: 玻璃、防火板、喷画、人造石
建筑面积: 280m²

1. The white flowers are in full bloom against the black background
2. Clear and free lines make a three-dimensional space better
3. The lighting designs set off the concise decorations and also articulate the personalized theme

1．白的花朵在黑的底色上怒放
2．线条明朗、奔放，让空间更为立体地呈现
3．灯光设计对空间简约的装饰进行了突出，也突出了空间个性化的主题

Design Concept:

As the fast–food restaurant has become one part of our life, how to bring art into fast–food restaurant space, create the art ambience in the dining space and make a kind of fast–food culture when improving people's life quality are the designer's initial concerns.

The management strategy of Lejia Fast–food Restaurant is youth, fashion and health. The designer hopes to create a modern spatial experience which is stylish and exquisite, offering the guests double enjoyment in taste and sense. The designs are employed to decorate the restaurant according to its themes and meanwhile create the uniqueness of this brand.

The situation and characters of this restaurant depend on its consumption group, which are mainly the bourgeois. Accordingly, the space must be of novel, fashionable and prominent .

1. Bright orange is the best masterstroke to animate the space
2. Compact layout improves the spatial limits within the building
1．鲜橙色是将空间点 "亮" 的最精彩的一笔
2．简约的格局改善了建筑内的空间局限

"Nature +Stylish Elements"is regarded as the design theme in this case. Nature arouses the comfortable and relaxed feeling while fashionable elements are the representatives of trend. Only the mix of both factors can completely achieve the designer's ideas. Naturalism is realized by using the fresh flavor, pure colors, natural conceptual materials and dynamic and free lines, which jointly define the pleasing and appealing space in this restaurant. Such elements as the black–and–white patterns and orange glass are randomly scattered in the space, delivering the fresh and natural concepts. The mutual contrast of orange, black–and–white patterns well reflects the spatial features —vigorous, pure and bright. The patterns and structure are like old trees, expressing the forceful connotation by simple lines. A variety of lamp shapes are the designer's fantastic symbols, which evoke a sense of mystery in the environment and create so many views in a leisure and dynamic dining atmosphere.

In this case, vivid colors, together with the neat lines perfectly convey the spatial fashionable feeling. Every kind of fashionable expression here becomes the spatial art invented by the designer.

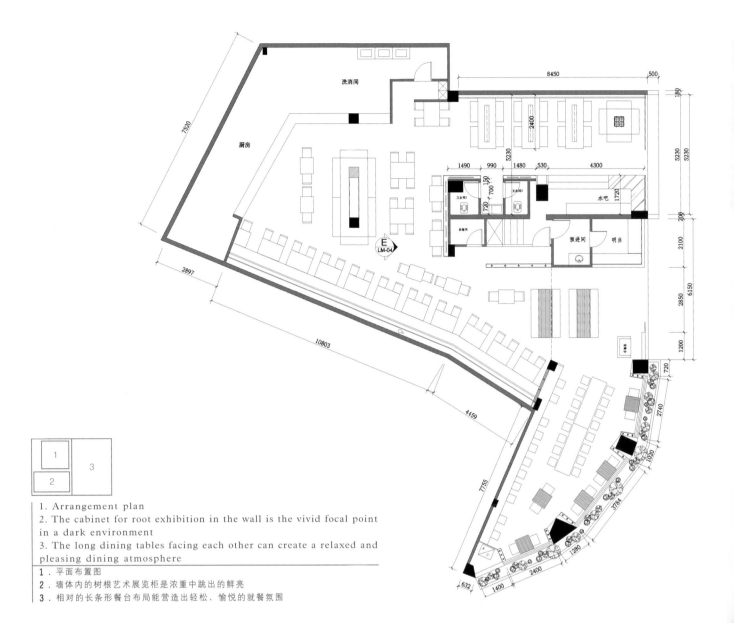

洗消间

厨房

水吧

预进间

明档

E
LM-04

1. Arrangement plan
2. The cabinet for root exhibition in the wall is the vivid focal point in a dark environment
3. The long dining tables facing each other can create a relaxed and pleasing dining atmosphere

1. 平面布置图
2. 墙体内的树根艺术展览柜是浓重中跳出的鲜亮
3. 相对的长条形餐台布局能营造出轻松、愉悦的就餐氛围

设计说明：

快餐厅已经成为我们生活中的一部分，怎样将艺术引入快餐厅空间，营造餐饮空间的艺术氛围，在提升人们生活质量的同时营造一种餐饮文化，这成为设计师最初考虑的问题。

乐嘉快餐厅的经营策略是年轻化、时尚化、健康化。设计师希望能营造一种时尚精致的摩登空间，提供给顾客口腹与视觉的双重享受。围绕此主题对餐厅进行"包装"，创造品牌的独特性。

本餐厅的地理位置与餐厅性质决定了其主要客户群为小资一族，因此空间诉求强调新颖、时髦、明亮的风格。

设计师以"自然＋流行元素"作为本案的创作主线。自然给人舒适、放松的感觉，流行元素是时尚的代表，两者结合才能最完整地实现设计师的构想。把自然主义以色彩纯真、意象自然的素材结合奔放、自由线条来表现，展现出乐嘉快餐厅愉悦人心的性感面貌。黑白图案、橙色的玻璃等元素在空间的肆意铺陈，传达出清新自然的自我主张，且鲜橙色与黑白相互对比、映衬，突出了朝气盎然且纯真明亮的空间个性。立面图案与硬体造型以古树根作为主题，从单纯线条中发掘出充满张力的内涵。丰富的灯具造型是设计师的奇想，让空间多了些许神秘的气息，织构出目不暇接的景致，营造出轻松活泼的用餐氛围。

本案以亮丽的色调，明朗的线条将空间的时尚感传达得很完美。当中各种传递时尚的方式成为设计师创造的一种空间艺术。

| 1 | 2 |
| | 3 |

1. The bare trunks express more tensile force
2. A palette of colors is employed to decorate this space, delivering the mysterious feeling
3. The square droplight is a confluence of Chinese traditional style and the modern stylish style
1．光秃秃的树干有着更强的张力
2．各种色彩在空间浸染开来，神秘感也蔓延着
3．方形吊灯是中式传统风格与现代时尚风格的结合体

Elegant Impression
雅致印象

Elegance mirrors a kind of life quality. No matter large or small, the elegant space presents a kind of thought.

雅致体现出一种生活质量，无论大雅还是小雅，它都是一种境界。

Title: Zi Jing Wan Modern Hotel
Designer: Song Guoliang
Design company: Ningbo Ruby Decoration Design Co.,Ltd.
Materials: Brown mirror, Oak veneer, Cloth art,
Crystal, Wall Cloth, Colored Glaze
Floor area: 1,800m²

项目名称： 紫鲸湾时尚酒店
设 计 师： 宋国梁
设计公司： 宁波红宝石装饰设计有限公司
主要饰材： 茶镜、橡木饰面板、布艺、水晶、墙布、琉璃
建筑面积： 1800m²

1. The restaurant facade is a mix of western style and modernity
2\3. The restaurant exterior view sets off by warm light

1．西洋气息与时尚感交融的酒店外观

2\3．暖色灯光映照下的餐厅外景

1. The purple curved seats and the small crystal floor lamp reflect the partitioned private space and the human concerns

1．紫色弧形餐位和小巧的水晶落地灯，体现了对私密空间的区域划分和人文关怀

Design Concept:

This is a modern restaurant composed of western canopy, colored glass, and decorative balcony. The interplay of light and lines constitute an elegant restaurant, where people can enjoy the delicious food and the romantic and vogue atmosphere.

The designer draws creative inspiration from the fascinating crystal and prepares the precise style and integrated designs for the hotel. Black and purple are the key tones to decorate the space. 2,500 shining crystal ornaments, superb furry decorations and modern fashion— show culture are combined to create a magnificent and graceful dining space. A feast of visual performance is presented here.

The 7.7−meter−high space is divided into three levels: the first and second levels are the ordinary dining areas while the third accommodates the compartments.

Due to the limit of width, the entrance design adopts one Chinese traditional gardening technique —" varying views when moving". The designer creates a circulation from the vestibule to the hall. The oblique mirror, stainless steel decorations, high glass door, exquisite glass knob are combined to form an exclusive entrance. The vestibule looks like a wood−and−glass box.

The capacious hall is very attractive. Silvery crystal chandelier, ikebana and ornaments are elaborately selected. The CHANEL leather bag advertisement boards replace the conventional decorative paintings. The brand is a status but also a prevailing trend. There are some decorative desks in the hall showing the modern and exaggerated features. Light purple velour and perforated decoration are luxuriant but concise.

The second level space basically echoes with the first one. There are small seats near the glazed hand railing. People can invite some bosom friends here commanding the view of the first level in this upper space.

The compartments on the third level have the unconventional layout. The glass and voile curtain are employed to partition the spaces, half hidden and half open. Black and purple colors run throughout the areas like the crystal ornaments. The VIP compartment is a mixed place including leather, rough stones, crystal, mirror and other materials, showing the magnificent but cultural ambience. The customized sofas, together with the high dining chair and wines on the wall are unique and exclusive. The designer brings the show window concept into the aisles. Leather, ornaments, fragrance and colorful drinking cups are grouped and match each other to show the meaningful artistic themes. People may feel strolling in a galaxy, where stars, super models and fashionable dresses walk down from the black−and−white fashion show pictures. This space teems with a touch of reminiscence and strong romantic feeling. Here, people can read the misted, modern and appealing love of crystal.

1. A large delicate advertisement picture acts as the backdrop behind the side-by-side sofas
2. The arrangement and decorations of the entire area show the classical beauty of European style to the utmost
3. 3rd floor arrangement plan
4. 2nd floor (mezzanine) arrangement plan
5. 1st floor arrangement plan

1．并排放置的沙发以大幅精美的广告画为背景
2．整个区域的布置和装饰尽展欧式风格设计的经典之美
3．三层平面布置图
4．二层（夹层）平面布置图
5．一层平面布置图

本案是一个现代新潮的餐饮酒店、西式遮雨篷、彩色玻璃、装饰阳台、交织的光与线条,组合出一个足够优雅的餐厅,让人在品尝着美食的同时也享受着浪漫与时尚。

设计师从水晶的迷幻中找到了本案的创作灵感,为酒店做了准确的风格定位和整体设计,并选择以黑色和紫色打造它尊贵的主调。2500颗水晶已经足够灿烂,毛皮饰物的华丽、时装文化的摩登,成功打造了一个厚重、高雅的餐饮空间,一场视觉盛宴。

酒店7.7米高的空间被分割成三层,一、二层为散座区,三层是包厢区。

受横向宽度的限制,入口的设计吸取了中国传统园林移步换景的特点,设计了一个先通过玄关区再进入大厅的动线,倾斜的镜面、不锈钢体块、超高的单扇玻璃门、精美的琉璃拉手,仅在入口就使人感受到它的与众不同,玄关看起来像由木、玻璃围成的盒子。

豁然开朗的大厅让人惊艳,银色水晶吊灯、插花等装饰品都经过了的精心挑选,CHANEL的皮包堂而皇之取代了传统的装饰画,可见品牌一种身份也是一种流行。大厅等待区的装饰延续了现代夸张的特点,浅紫色的丝绒面料背后隔断的镂雕花饰,华丽而不失简约。

二层空间基本用于满足与一层空间互动,靠近玻璃栏杆处设计了小餐位,邀两三好友来聚,居高临下,一层风光尽收眼底。

三层包厢群不再是传统意义上的格局,用玻璃纱缦隔成半隐半露的空间,黑色、紫色,如水一样贯穿了其间。VIP包厢采用了皮革、粗石、水晶、镜面等材料组合,华贵中不失人文,特制沙发、加高设计的餐椅、嵌入墙面的红酒柜,独有的和惟一的。设计师把商业橱窗的概念运用到走廊公共空间中来,毛皮、饰品、香熏花、彩色酒杯,经过分类与搭配,形成了一个个完美的艺术主题,让人俨然走进了一个艺术长廊;黑白时装画成了空间的明星,名模、时装纷纷走进来,婉约、淡淡的怀旧色彩与浓郁的浪漫情怀弥散开来。徜徉其间,阅读那份迷离、摩登,还有醉人的水晶恋情。

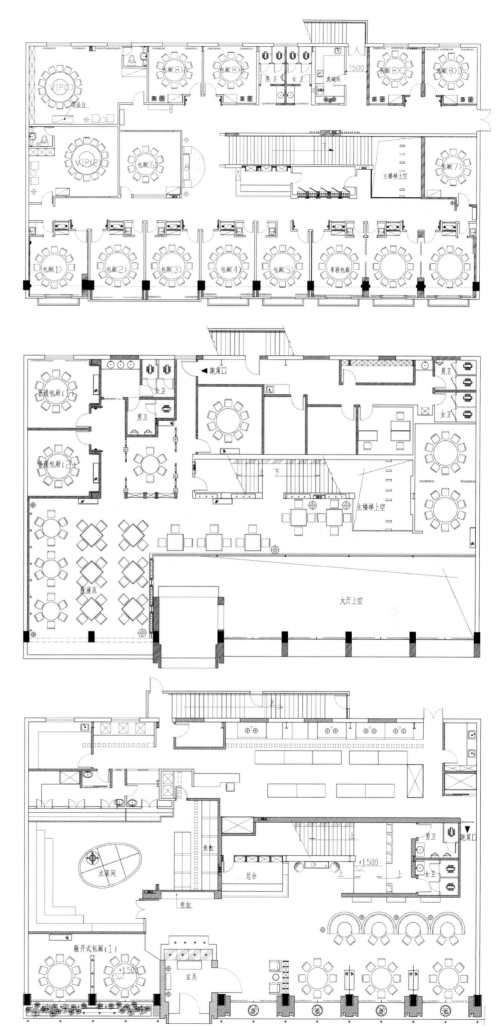

| 1 | | 3 |
| 2 | | 4 |

1. The crystal droplight and the floor lamp ma[ke] the space exquisite and magnificent
2. The broad advertisement picture on the wall mal[e] the space more graceful
3. The window in VIP room gives a touch of reminiscen[ce]
4. Wine cabinet on the wall

1．水晶吊灯与落地灯彰显空间的精致与华贵
2．墙面大幅的广告画为空间增添了高雅气质
3．VIP 房的窗户给人以怀旧的感觉
4．嵌入墙体的酒柜

1. This is the iridescent space composed of crystal decorations
2. The crystal on the tree is like the little flowers in blossom and evokes the spring flavor in the interior space

1．水晶饰品打造的璀璨空间
2．树上挂满的水晶如"开"着的淡淡的小花，将春天的气息"诱入"室内

1. The well-arranged performance of light and the shadow of lighting
2. Wine cabinet functions as a partition
3. Aisle
4. The high steps extend upwards and purple acrylics patterns on the wall are very charming

1．灯光的明暗处理恰到好处

2．酒柜隔断

3．走道

4．高高的台阶延伸上去，墙壁上紫色的亚克力雕花图案散发着迷人的光彩

The Noble in Modesty
朴素贵族

An elegance of simplicity in coordination with a noble air gives prominence to a friendly and amiable atmosphere.

极朴素的典雅与恰到好处的贵族气质融合，突出了空间的融合力与亲切感。

Title: Flaus Western Dining Hall
Designer: Liu Jie
Materials: Walnut timber，Glass，Stone
Floor area: 325m²

项目名称: 福莱仕西餐厅
设 计 师: 刘杰
主要饰材: 胡桃木、玻璃、洞石
建筑面积: *325m²*

1. Against the black greenish velvet, a fresh air pervades in the soft light
2. The orange glass which divides the kitchen and the restaurant is the most striking feature of the space
3. Creativity is fully expressed in the droplight designing

1．墨绿色的丝绒靠背，在柔和灯光的映衬下弥漫着一种清新脱俗的优雅
2．隔开厨房与餐厅的橙红色玻璃，是空间最亮丽的一抹色彩
3．吊灯的设计创意十足

Design Concept:

Flaus Western Dining Hall is a sumptuous one which can hold 116 people at one time. With its particular feature and tasteful environment, it gives an atmosphere of relaxation to the customers.

A series of cream–white hues play the main role in coordination with dark colors of the wallboard and the walnut timber furniture, textured stones and soft greenish velour are further complement of brightness and shades.

The materials of the restaurant are all presented unfinished — neither carved nor decorated, however, the beauty is by no means weakened.

On the whole, through simple lines, modest layout, refined lighting, ar careful arrangement as well, it creates a harmonious and elegant dinir space.

It is distinctive that the kitchen of the restaurant is an open style whic enables people to see through the orange glass.

This case is characterized by the meticulous arrangement and particul decoration.

1	2

1. Dark wall and light-colored paintings coordinate each other harmoniously
2. The strong contrast between dark and light colors making the space elegant and stable

1．深色的墙体与浅色的艺术画和谐搭配
2．深色调和浅色调的强烈对比，空间显得既雅致又稳重

1. The graceful decoration and lighting furnish the sidewalk with elegance
2. The timber partition helps to form a more orderly space
3. A corner of the Dining Hall
4. Arrangement plan

1. 考究的装饰与灯光的设计让走道有着典雅的气质
2. 原木的隔断让空间更有序
3. 餐厅一隅
4. 平面布置图

设计说明:

福莱仕西餐厅是一个能容纳116人同时用餐的豪华餐厅。其独具特色、雅致的环境能使顾客备感愉悦轻松且富有激情。

餐厅使用了一系列乳白色作为空间的色彩基调,并搭配胡桃木家具和墙板的深色调,粗面的洞石与质感柔软的墨绿色丝绒配以精致的餐具,空间亮色与适度的暗影实现自然互补。

餐厅的材料均以原始的面貌呈现,不加雕琢、不施粉黛,却丝毫没有削弱其美观效果。整体而言,本案运用简洁的线条,朴素的摆设,考究的细节布置,合理的灯光配置,来营造一个和谐而高雅的用餐空间。

比较独特的是,餐厅的厨房进行了开敞设计,透过橙红色玻璃人们可以看到厨师们的活动。

精心构思的布局和对于细节装饰的特别关注是本案的特色所在。

1. Elevation 1
2. The glimmering dinner service and elegant candlestick in the light represent the high status of the restaurant
3. Elevation 2

1．立面图1
2．精致的餐具、烛台在灯光下光泽闪烁,彰显出餐厅的档次
3．立面图2

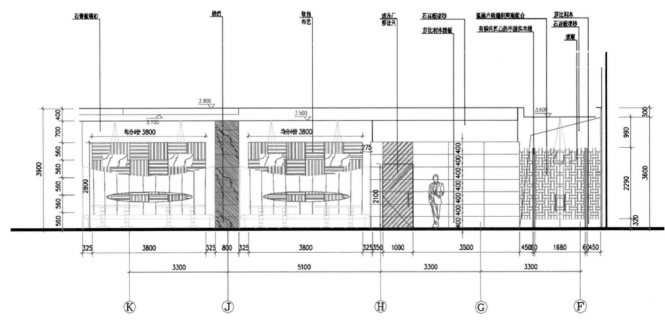

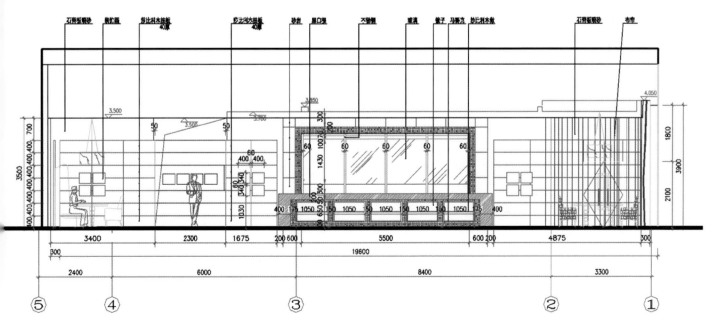

Life Style of Petit Bourgeois
小资生活

Dining at different places means tasting various experience, and life thus gets rich and colorful.
不同的餐饮空间给人不同的生活体验，人生因此而变得丰富多彩。

Title: Steamship "Minghua" Park Lane Pub
Desinger: Qin Yueming
Design Company: Shenzhen Rongor Design Consulting Co.,Ltd.
Materials: Mosaic，Cement，Lace curtains，Stainless steel，Dark mirrors and Glass.
Floor area: 580m²

项目名称: "明华轮" 柏宁酒吧
设 计 师: 秦岳明
设计公司: 深圳市朗联设计顾问有限公司
主要饰材: 马赛克、素水泥、纱帘、不锈钢、黑镜、清玻
建筑面积: 580m²

1. Background wall is tastefully designed
2. An irresistible appeal from lighting

1. 背景墙的设计独特而颇具情调
2. 灯光暧昧，让人不知不觉迷醉于其间

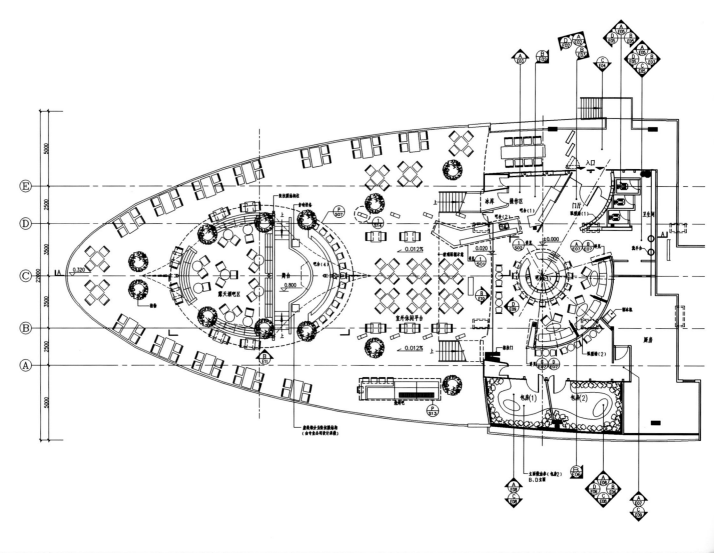

1. Arrangement plan
2. Diverse techniques make its mysteriousness
3. In the airy light, a sort of petit bourgeois atmosphere pervades the space where a raised sidetable is placed next to the large mirror

1．平面布置图
2．诸多设计手法的运用使空间给人变幻莫测的神秘感
3．大块的镜面旁放置高脚椅和抬高的小桌，灯光迷离，一种小资的情调在空间弥漫开来

1. Shadow and the holes strewn on the wall exert a magical fascination
2. The crystal bead curtain emits a sense of elegance and dignity
1．墙上的投影与圆洞错落分布，让空间充满变幻感
2．晶莹剔透的珠帘在灯光下透着高贵和典雅

Design Concept:

Steamship "Minghua", originally a deluxe passenger ship of Guangzhou Ocean Company, is later moored at Shekou, Shenzhen, becoming a permanent touring spot on land. This case, a pub–style restaurant, is located on the fourth deck on Steamship "Minghua" Hotel in Sea World, Shenzhen. Considering the fact that it is transformed from a passenger ship, the designer, taking advantage of the ship shape, adopts a unique technique to treat the space as a slant, keeping balance with the external lines while the interior is centered on the circular bar. A sort of extension from point to line is highlighted by furnishing separate sections with different forms and textures. Here, black and white rule over the theme when the use of other colors in proportion to the change of textures enriches the special quality in a reasonable way.

The unique aura of pub is enchanting; life here is sweet and special.

| 1 | 2 | 3 |

1. Details stand for quality
2. A sense of modern is felt all around
3. Lighting and decorative details give expression to dimensions

1．细节彰显品质
2．现代气息无处不在
3．布光与装饰细节让空间充满立体感

设计说明：

华轮，原为广州远洋公司的豪华客轮，后停泊于深圳蛇口成为永久性的岸上游景点。本案位于深圳蛇口海上世界"明华轮"酒店甲板四层，是一个酒吧餐厅。由于建筑本身就是由豪华客轮改造而成，结合船体原有结构，设计师用独特的空间处理手法，使入口门厅与吧台的动线呈斜角处理，保持与室外线自然衔接，并以圆形的中心吧台作为室内空间的中心。作为船体原有的元"圆"这个主题被设计师重复运用于整个酒吧空间中。根据不同的功能区域理成不同形式与质感的圆形造型，实现了由点到线及面的延伸。黑与白成为个空间的色彩主题。不同的色彩比例关系及材料质感的变化在保持统一的同又保证了空间的丰富性，符合空间使用功能的表情。

厅独有的酒吧情调，让人在迷醉的氛围中享受生活，品味别样人生。

Chinese Style

中式风格

Cultural Dynasty
文化王朝

A dining space without culture is just like a beauty who wears garish clothes but is not well-educated, which seems dull and boring. A successful restaurant design should be a cultural stage with potential exploration and performance.

没有文化的餐饮空间设计，好比衣着花哨不重内在修养的伊人，显得苍白无趣。成功的餐饮空间设计则一定是挖掘了一个可以涵养的文化母体，加以发挥和渲染。

Title: Lingdian Restaurant in Hongli Huangchao Hotel
Designer: Feng Jiayun
Design company: Shang Rui Yuan Zhu Design and Production Co.,Ltd.
Materials: Stone，Timber facing，Wallpaper，Floor，Carpet，Latex paint，Stucco
Floor area: 500m²

项目名称: 泓历皇朝大酒店零点餐厅
设 计 师: 冯嘉云
设计公司: 上瑞元筑设计制作有限公司
主要饰材: 石材、木饰面、墙纸、地板、地毯、乳胶漆、灰泥
建筑面积: 500m²

1. A vermeil door makes the aisle overflow with the rich and honor effect
2. A hall of great manner
3. Stylish expression in a Chinese style environment
1．朱红色的大门让走道洋溢着富贵气息
2．气派的大堂
3．中式空间的时尚表达

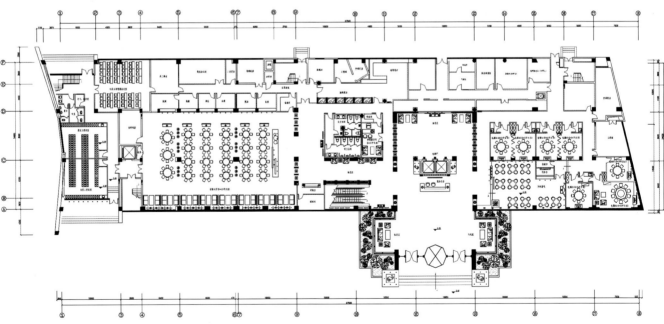

1		4
2	3	5

1. A lounge in the graceful and comfortable elevator lobby
2. 1st floor arrangement plan
3. 1st floor loft arrangement plan
4. The black-and-white photos on the wall conjure up the memory
5. One corner of the elegant lounge

1. 优雅、舒适的电梯厅休息区
2. 一层平面布置图
3. 一层阁楼平面布置图
4. 墙面的黑白照片引发回忆
5. 典雅休息区的一角

Design Concept:

This restaurant of the mixed East–West style possesses not only the traditional beauty of Chinese style, but also the fashionable decoration of modern style, which implies that the history and modernity are in perfect harmony here. This capacious time–theme background adds grandeur into this area.

The design of Lingdian Restaurant boast modernity and fashion as its theme. Large–scale silver foil decoration makes the top space neat and beautiful, so that the top mutually sets off the brilliant crystal art hangings. Completely filled with the modern flavor, the entire space creates a graceful and grand ambience that sets this space apart from other concise space. The use of a Chinese screen articulates the multiple layers of these catering space and meanwhile reflects the design themes of the entire restaurant — modern Chinese style, which is neatness and fashion. The restrained colors in this ambience also harmonize and blend in with the accretion of history brought by Chinese elements.

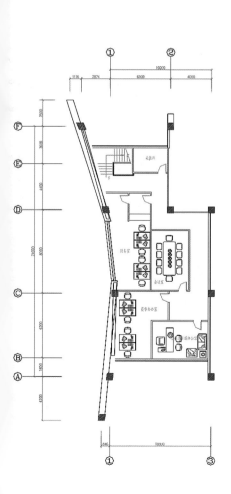

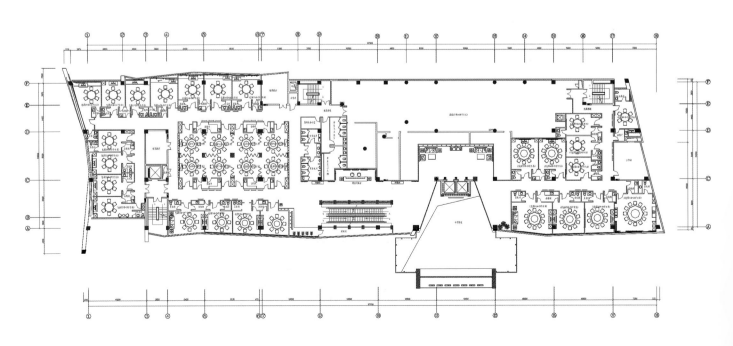

1	3
2	4

1. Meander patterns on the carpet are the symbols of Chinese style
2. 2nd floor arrangement plan
3. Chinese screen, theatrical mask, crystal ornaments and bright red sofas are the elements combining tradition with vogue
4. 3rd floor arrangement plan

1 . 地毯上的回字纹是中式风格的象征
2 . 二层平面布置图
3 . 中式屏风、戏剧脸谱、水晶饰品、大红沙发，实现了传统与时尚的融合
4 . 三层平面布置图

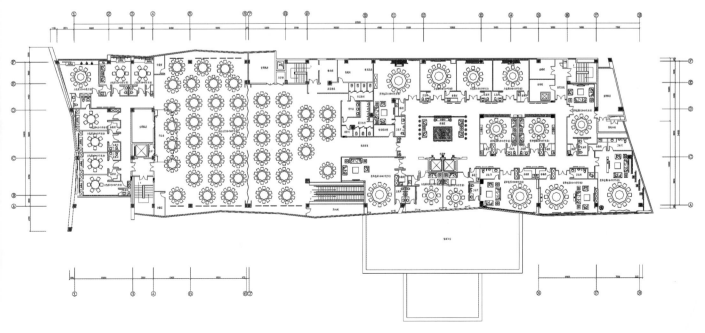

设计说明:

中西糅合的餐厅空间既具备了中式风格的传统美，又具备现代风格的时尚感，两者的融合，将历史与现代沟通。这个广阔的时光主题，让空间颇具气势。

零点餐厅以现代时尚为设计基调，大面积的银箔贴顶让顶部空间整洁、美观，与闪烁着晶莹光泽的水晶艺术挂件相映衬，将整个空间的现代气息烘托得淋漓尽致。中式元素屏风的运用使就餐区平面更显层次感，并将整个餐厅现代、中式、简洁、时尚的设计主题表现出来。空间的色调较为沉稳，这是与中式元素所带有的历史的厚重感相协调、相交融的。

1	2

1. The splendid crystal hangings, together with flamboyant colors greatly glorify the space
2. The elevator lobby has exclusive features

1. 华贵的水晶艺术挂件、艳丽的色调，极力地让空间得到张扬
2. 电梯厅的风景亦非同一般

Heaven and Earth
天地一家

"The person who wants to possess the most excellent thing in the world should first get its soul and then its essence". The success of restaurant design is also attributed to the key elements — soul and essence.

"欲得天下之大美者，必先得其心，必先得其志"，餐饮空间设计的成功，亦以得其"心"、"志"为关键。

Title: Tian Di Yi Jia
Designer: Yu Qingshan
Design company: Norman Design
Materials: Flashed brick, Stone carving, Wood
Floor area: 2,000m²

项目名称：天地一家
设 计 师：余青山
设计公司：山川设计事务所
主要饰材：青砖、石雕、木材
建筑面积：2000m²

	2
1	3

1. The slim plants on the table and the outdoor green
bamboos interestingly speak to each other
2. Courtyard
3. Several seal sculptures

1．桌上纤细的植物与户外的翠竹相映成趣
2．庭院
3．几个印章雕塑

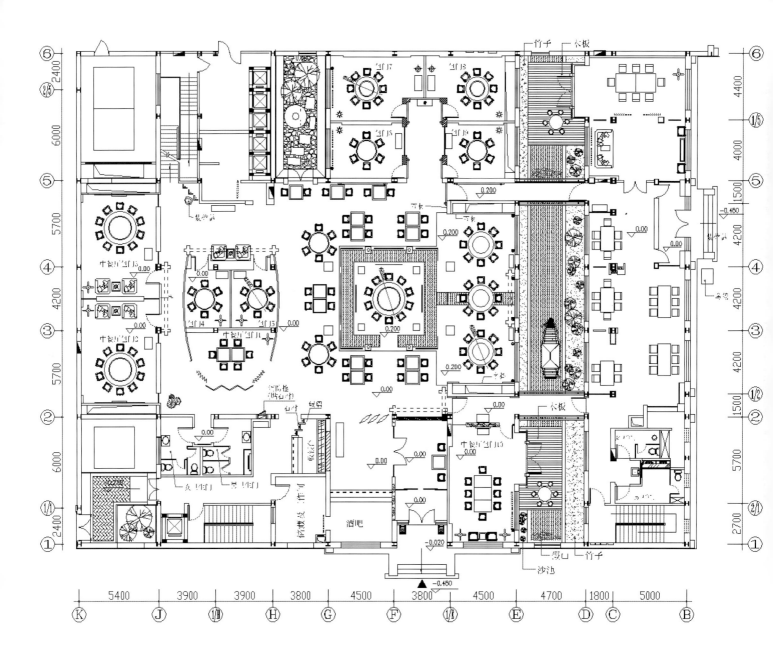

Design Concept:

This restaurant is close to the Imperial Palace, and the original building is a traditional Beijing compound with a glass light well in it. According to the characteristics of the original building, the designer makes use of the natural rays of the original building. A square is placed to symbolize the earth; the valance is hung over the lighting glass to symbolize the cloud; the four corners of the square are displayed with Azure Dragon (East), White Tiger (West), Vermilion Bird (South), Murky Warrior (North) to symbolize the directions of the earth, like the seal of the emperor signing on the center of the restaurant. The artful use of the Chinese traditional building and the art elements make the guests taste the spatial historical cultural connotation and the fashionable environment.

The whole space takes the areas in the hall with daylight as its principal axis, with the Beijing Changpu River in the channel around this principal axis, thereby making the environmental center more dazzling and striking owing to the light, the river and the garden. The whole space, with the embellishment of the center, appears very gorgeous. The space expands towards the four directions and employs stone and glass in the compartment in a solid and void way, making the transition and roundabout effect in space, and the people unable to see the entire space

1. 1st floor arrangement plan
2. The red voile curtain adds more charm in this antique space
3. The limpid water meanders with historical content
4. This is a Chinese classical lounge with a wooden wine rack as the background

1．一层平面布置图
2．红色纱帘为古色古香的空间增添风韵
3．一湾清水在"历史"中蜿蜒而行
4．以木质酒架为背景墙的中式古典风格的休息区

in a glance. Every space connects with each other without closed environment, which enlarges the visual effect of the space virtually, adding the sense of layer. On the second floor, the designer makes good use of the big balcony as the teahouse where people not only can taste the tea but also watch the cultural historic site — the Imperial Palace. That is so marvelous and appealing. The newly–built glazed roof and the partition, the interior greenery, the coarse rock and hewn stone, the tiny stream, and background music drawing people's spirit, all of these make everybody reluctant to leave.

Paying attention to the details is another characteristic of this case. The designer uses the design technique of the modern popular space and puts the emphasis on the details. All the furniture and decoration of Chinese style have lives, and they can improve or even change the atmosphere of one place. The designer has a special inventive mind, and chooses some Chinese style elements as one part of the entirety, such as the valance of the Imperial Palace, the calligraphy and painting of the celebrities, the seal of the emperor, the civilian and the military officer etc, which all belong to the upper–class. All of these make the space harmonious, sangfroid and rich in levels. The traditional aesthetic perception gets a new annotation through this style of decoration here. The modern Chinese style can often get a decorative effect that the scenery changes when moving.

In the entire spatial design, the designer skillfully controls the relationship between elegance and popularity, tradition and fashion, to create a spatial environment that shocks everyone.

1. Two silk cushions unconsciously reveal the modernity of space
2. Carvings, reading lamp and curtain are delicate and elegant
3. Removing the restaurant into the courtyard full of sunshine
4. The calligraphy on the wall makes the space graceful
5. Elegant exterior view
6. The washroom is a mix of classicism and modernity
7. Exquisite paintings and well-designed Chinese furniture highlight the elegant Chinese classical space

1 . 两个丝绸面料的靠垫无意中展现了空间的时尚感
2 . 雕刻、台灯、窗帘，每一个装饰都精致而典雅
3 . 将餐厅搬到洒满阳光的庭院
4 . 墙面的书法作品让空间充满雅趣
5 . 清雅的外景
6 . 古典与时尚融合的洗手间
7 . 雅致的装饰画，中规中矩的中式家具，凸现了中式古典空间的典雅

设计说明:

本餐厅邻近故宫,原建筑是一个传统的北京院落,院内设有玻璃采光井。设计师根据原建筑的特征,利用原建筑获得的自然光线,把四周布置成方形,象征大地。采光玻璃的上方布满帷幔,象征云。方形的四角用青龙、白虎、朱雀、玄武装饰品陈设,象征大地的方向,犹如皇帝的印章,印在餐厅的中心。通过对中国传统建筑与艺术元素的巧妙运用,使宾客感受到空间的历史文化内涵和环境的时尚。

整个空间以天光投入大厅为主轴,北京菖蒲河被引入了主轴的周围,有光、有水、有庭园,环境的中心因此更加耀眼夺目。整个空间在中心的渲染之下,呈现出一派繁荣昌盛的景象。空间向四周扩展,隔间采用石材与玻璃并用的手法,虚实相间,使空间产生转换、迂回的效果,让人无法一眼尽观全场。每个空间彼此有串连而不闭封,无形中取得空间加大的视觉效果,增加层次感。二层空间中,充分利用原建筑的大露台做茶座,使人在品茶的同时又可观赏到故宫这一文化古迹,别有一番情趣。新加建的玻璃顶及隔墙,室内绿化,粗岩毛石,涓涓细流,勾人魂魄的背景音乐,令人留连忘返。

注重细节是本设计的又一特点,设计师运用现代时尚空间的设计手法,同时加强对细节的关注,每一件中式家具、装饰品都是有生命的,它们能改善甚至改变一个地方的气质。设计师独具匠心,选择了一些中式元素作为整体的一部分,如皇宫的帷幔、名人字画、皇帝及文工武卫等显贵人物的印章等,使空间气氛变得和谐、泰然,层次丰富。传统的审美观念,在这种装饰风格中得到了新的诠释,现代中式风格,往往可以达到移步换景的效果。

在整个空间设计中,设计师巧妙地把握了高雅与流行,传统与时尚之间的关系,创造出令人震撼的又一空间环境。

1		4
2		
3		5

1. The table reflects simplicity in modern designs
2. The beauty of balance is embodied in the symmetric designs of compartment
3. Two lamps on the high ceiling are very exquisite and magnificent
4. Two bright red sofas in the dim light seem to tell an old story
5. 2nd floor arrangement plan

1. 餐桌布置——古朴中的现代
2. 包房的设计讲究对称的平衡之美
3. 高高地吊在顶部的两盏灯精致而华贵
4. 两个大红的沙发,在幽暗的光线中静默如一段古老、尘封的故事
5. 二层平面布置图

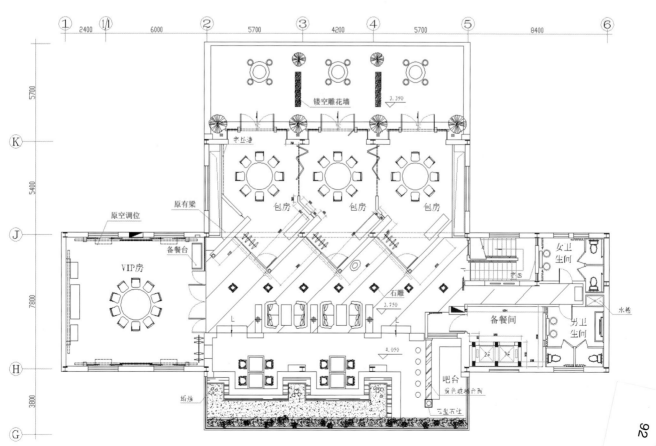

① 2400 ①1 6000 ② 5700 ③ 4200 ④ 5700 ⑤ 8400 ⑥

镂空雕花墙 3.390

Ⓚ

包房 包房 包房

Ⓙ 原空调位 原有梁 备餐台 女卫生间

VIP房 石雕 3.750 男卫生间 水桶

备餐间

Ⓗ 吧台 染色玻璃台面

蜡烛 云型石柱

Ⓖ

Neoclassical Space
新古典空间

Is modernity the permanent opposite of classicism? In a modern restaurant, modernity well harmonizes with classicism just like the fish and water. People in this place can enjoy the double experience.

谁说时尚和古典是永久的对立者？在现代的餐饮空间里，时尚与古典如鱼与水般相融，让来此享受的人们既得"鱼"，又得"熊掌"。

Title: Ningbo Zui Mei Fashion Restaurant
Designer: Wan Hongwei，Yu Nuo，Hu Dawei
Design company: Heaven Design
Materials: Wood，Glass
Floor area: 1,500m²

项目名称: 宁波醉美时尚餐厅
设 计 师: 万宏伟、余诺、胡达维
设计公司: 汉文设计
主要饰材: 木材、玻璃
建筑面积: 1500m²

	2
1	3

1. A unique lamp surrounded by water lilies is just like the king of flower
2. The raised atrium area in the center helps with guiding the people and making an accessible hall with multiple levels
3. The porch at the entrance doesn't directly lead to the lobby due to a shear wall but instead makes an imposing area. The curved floor-to-ceiling glass window extends to the mirror on the main wall creating the void and solid effect

1．在荷花簇拥中的造型奇特的灯具俨然一朵盛开的花王
2．抬升的中部中庭区域，使大厅空间有了方向的引导性，也使空间有了更多层次
3．入口处的门厅虽与大厅因剪力墙而无法贯通，反而让门厅空间有了隆重的意味，主体墙面的镜子延伸了弧形落地玻璃窗，虚实难分

Design Concept:

Expansion and Refashionment

The designer when designing pays great attention to a row of long windows and the enough wide space, which is 4.5 meters high, because they can bring many possibilities of expansion to the space, and they are available for the refashionment of the spatial level.

Excavating the essence of the space, the designer establishes the hall of corridor type as the body part, uses the VIP boxes to gather the space, emphasizes the traverse and the torch, makes divisions between the transition region and the buffer zone, conceals the unnecessary columns in the atrium of the box region and conforms the division to have a clear and good space for dining. Partially uplifting the VIP box region and the atrium area not only brings the sense of level to the space, but also makes the hall "descend". The elevation of the hall oblique top as well as the lowered flat top around it because of the factor of the air pipes, which caters to the collective spatial manufacture to make the high hall of corridor style much higher and farther, and to have new visual experience in VIP boxes which are ascended.

On the premise of the satisfaction of function, the space is promoted and enriched in style. Material quality, light and bold colors are indeed important, but the layout of the actual space is the most important. The combination and arrangement of the four groups of encircled region in the hall changes the common dining style in Chinese restaurants, bringing the new experience of dining to the fashion feeling —eating the Chinese food in the western way. The symmetrical pattern not only echoes with the shaft-type suspended ceiling, but also brings magnificent and strong flavor to the dining atmosphere.

Concept and Element

No imitation of the tradition laying in the traditional way, the designer withdraws the well-content decorative pattern and design of the Chinese classical tradition, carves for the formation or carving on different materials such as stone surface and wood surface etc, or repeatedly ranges the designs that are suitable for the ordering carpet of the boxes, which not only emphasizes the decorative characteristic, but also shows classic fashion elements.

1. Thanks to the design of a central island-style compartment, the four superfluous columns can be hidden, which not only makes an integrated and neat space but also produces more changes in this area
2. Viewed from the aisle, the raised VIP compartment is very neat and passionate
3. It is very interesting to see the classical traditional ornaments meet and echo with several flowers

1．中部岛式包厢区隐藏了四根立柱，使空间更干净利落，岛式布局又使空间有了更多的变化
2．从过道看抬升的VIP包厢内景，工整中透出热情
3．古典传统的装饰元素"遇见"几束鲜花，两者相得益彰，情趣十足

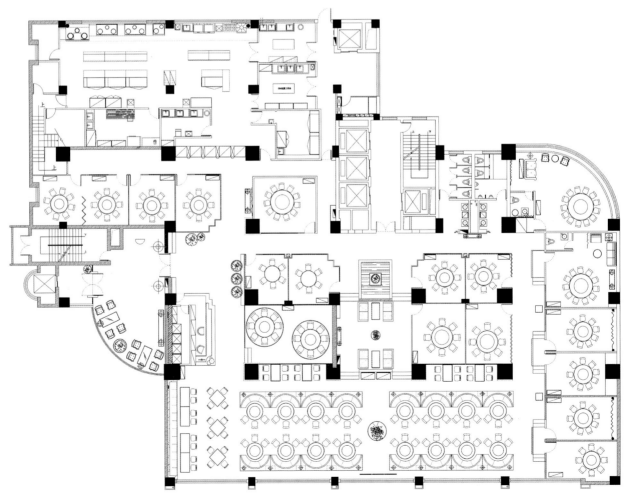

| 1 | 3 |
| 2 | 4 |

1. Viewed from the lobby center, the elevated area brings in various visual experiences
2. Arrangement plan
3. The enclosed dining mode and symmetrical layout in the lobby give an imposing and splendid effect
4. The concise washroom

1．从大厅中部看中厅抬升区域，具有不同的视觉感受
2．平面布置图
3．大厅围合式就餐方式，布局对称，带来隆重华丽的意味
4．简洁的洗手间局部

The designer makes good use of the combination of the Chinese color using brownish-black wood and the black floor as the tone in the spat atmosphere, choosing the Chinese red and dark blue as the main color and controlling the color saturation as well as the assignment of the quanti quite appropriately.

The designer chooses the lotus as the decorative element for the restaura adding human breath to it. Also the traditional old-style family's furnitu are ordered, giving the black tone a modern comprehension and bringi a neoclassic flavor.

1	

1. The spacious corridor-style lobby strengthens the high level. The succinct and vigorous column surfaces are designed in the solid and void manner, stable and demure

1．大气开阔的廊式大厅。强调挑高的层高感受，简洁有力的立柱立面虚实结合，稳重大气

romotion and Conformity

aving got the succinct and vigorous spatial frame, the designer concisely xpresses the measurement of purity, the texture of material and the analysis of ght and shadow. As for a fashionable dining space, more emotion design is eeded to realize the expression of the happiness. The promotion of the mosphere brings the most direct drama tension to the dining space. The choices f the lamps and lanterns, the atmosphere of the lighting, the expansion and ontraction of the colors, the combination and alienation of the family private ecoration and so on, together with the conformity space and the spatial mosphere move people visibly and invisibly.

1

1. The atrium area and lobby are partitioned by a bead curtain, achieving the sunk effect and better raising the high level of the lobby

1．中庭区域与大厅间用珠帘隔离，一线之隔，让大厅有了下沉感，使大厅层高得以更好抬升

设计说明:

拓展．再造

设计师在设计时锁定了空间内层高4.5米的足够开敞的空间及通排的长窗，因为它们给空间带来很多拓展的可能，亦有利于空间层次的再造。

挖掘空间的内核，确立长廊式大厅主体。以VIP包厢区围合空间，强调人行走廊及过廊，划分空间过渡区域及灰空间带，在中庭包厢区内掩饰多余的立柱，干净利索地划分用餐空间。局部抬升VIP包厢区及中庭区域，既给空间带来层次感，又使大厅"下沉"，而大厅顶部斜顶的升高及周围因风管因素而降低的平顶，让挑高的廊式大厅更高远，而抬升的VIP包厢内也有了更新的视觉体验。

在满足功能的前提下，对空间加以形式上的丰富。材质、灯光及色彩固然重要，但实际上空间的布局才是最重要的。大厅四组围合式区域的排列，一改中餐厅的用餐局式，以中菜西吃的时尚感带来用餐新体验。而对称的格局，既呼应了中轴式吊顶，又给用餐气氛带来华贵而浓重的意味。

概念．元素

不做传统的照搬与堆砌，设计者提取中国古典传统如意花纹图案，雕刻成形或雕刻于石面、木面等不同材质上，或以图案在包厢地毯上进行反复排列，强调装饰性的同时，也带出古典时尚元素。

设计者对中国传统色彩加以组合，在大厅中运用棕黑色木材及黑色地面作为色彩基调，选用中国红及深蓝作为主色彩，根据色彩饱合度适度分配。

选取荷花作为餐厅的装饰元素，增加人文气息。传统旧式家具的铺设，在黑色的基调上以现代的方式加以理解，带来新古典韵味。

提升．整合

有了简洁有力的空间框架结构，设计者对纯粹的体量，材料肌理，进行简明的表达，也对光影进行了分析。但对于时尚感的餐饮空间，需要更多的情感设计，实现一种愉悦心情的表述。氛围的提升带来用餐空间最直接的戏剧张力。灯具，灯光的调节；色彩的扩张与收敛，家具和饰品的组合与分离等等，给人以有形或无形的感动。

1\3. VIP compartment with bright and strong colors
2. The bead curtains are sheafed or scattered with different flavors

1\ 3. 色彩饱和的VIP包厢
2．垂挂的珠帘、或束起或散开，各具风情

Tale
传说

There are a good many meaningful and beautiful tales in Chinese culture of food. The catering spaces decorated with traditional culture are just like tales that produce the timeless charm.

中国饮食文化中有诸多隽永、优美的传说，被传统文化包装的餐饮空间就如同传说一般，获得了无法被时间削减的魅力。

Title: Donghai Huayuan Hegang Japanese Restaurant
Designer: Liu Weijun
Design company: PINKI
Materials: Fraxinus mandshurica，Wallpaper，
Mirror，Featured stone，Carpet
Floor area: 300m²

项目名称：东海花园鹤港料理店
设 计 师：刘卫军
设计公司：深圳市品伊设计顾问有限公司
主要饰材：水曲柳、墙纸、镜子、文化石、地毯
建筑面积：*300m²*

1. It is the exquisite porcelain, elegant atmosphere and delicious food that accompany you to enjoy the hours
2. Two separate dinning areas have different flavors
3. Repeated performance of round patterns in this space has symbolic meaning

1. 精致的瓷器、典雅的环境、美味的食物，给您一段尽情享受生活的时光
2. 被分隔开的两个就餐区域，风情各异
3. "圆"在空间反复出现，颇具象征意义

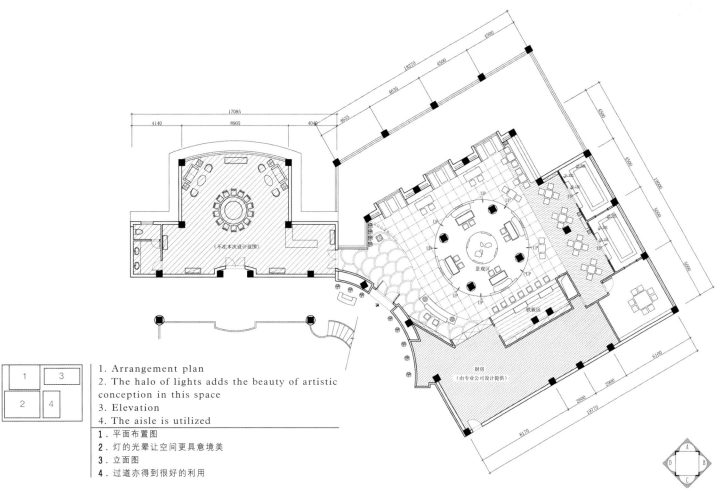

1. Arrangement plan
2. The halo of lights adds the beauty of artistic conception in this space
3. Elevation
4. The aisle is utilized

1. 平面布置图
2. 灯的光晕让空间更具意境美
3. 立面图
4. 过道亦得到很好的利用

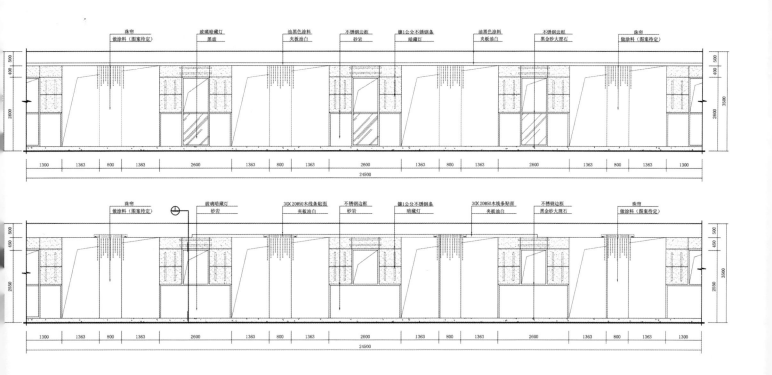

珠帘
做涂料（图案待定）　玻璃暗藏灯 黑玻　油黑色涂料 夹板油白　不锈钢边框 砂岩　镶1公分不锈钢条 暗藏灯　油黑色涂料 夹板油白　不锈钢边框 黑金砂大理石　珠帘 做涂料（图案待定）

500 / 400 / 2600 / 3500

1300 | 1363 | 800 | 1363 | 2600 | 1363 | 800 | 1363 | 2600 | 1363 | 800 | 1363 | 2600 | 1363 | 800 | 1363 | 1300
24500

珠帘 做涂料（图案待定）　玻璃暗藏灯 砂岩　30X20#50木线条贴面 夹板油白　不锈钢边框 砂岩　镶1公分不锈钢条 暗藏灯　30X20#50木线条贴面 夹板油白　不锈钢边框 黑金砂大理石　珠帘 做涂料（图案待定）

500 / 450 / 2550 / 3500

1300 | 1363 | 800 | 1363 | 2600 | 1363 | 800 | 1363 | 2600 | 1363 | 800 | 1363 | 2600 | 1363 | 800 | 1363 | 1300
24500

Design Concept:

When you open the door of Hegang, what bursts into the view is a space like the Japanese cortile in the open air. The spatial layout and decorations are extremely exquisite and artistic to show the restaurant's taste and individuality, which evoke the infinite imagination. This project is a modern Chinese style restaurant, in which there are a lot of Chinese traditional cultural elements interspersed. The culture of Han and Tang Dynasties are perfectly embodied here. The meander patterns, together with the vivid crane are skillfully employed here as the spatial themes, which endow the Hegang Japanese Restaurant with strong cultural background and artistic conception. That is "Where there is an artistic conception, there is a high quality". So, to create the beauty of artistic conception becomes the key concept in this case.

The restaurant lies in the clubhouse of Donghai Huayuan. In order to enlarge the area and create a capacious environment with interactive quality, four columns decorated with golden cranes and clouds are placed towards the top in the spatial layout. In addition, the transparent crystal bead curtains in four directions envelop a round space and shape the visual center in the entire restaurant. Owing to the rich culture of Han and Tang Dynasties, the colors are mostly purple, green, golden and black which set off by the lighting to create unique and beautiful spatial effect.

Within the cortile, people can smell the aroma of salmon in the air. There are dark Manchurian-tree wood, mosaic flooring, hanging bead curtain, and uneven featured stone here. The designs coming from the Japanese lifestyle achieve dramatic performance in each corner of Hegang.

1. Light acts as the spice of restaurant
2. Dark colors make a stable and generous dining space
3. The decorations of different layers produce the layered beauty
4. Light, bead curtain, crystal ornament and bonsai together constitute a classical and elegant restaurant
5. To see a world in a flower

1．灯光亦是餐厅的调味品
2．深沉的色调让就餐区显得沉稳、大气
3．不同层次不同的装饰，产生层层叠叠的美
4．灯光、珠帘、水晶饰物、盆景，呈现一个古典、雅致的餐厅
5．一花一世界

设计说明：

当您推开鹤港的大门，映入眼帘的是一个给人以日式露天内院感觉的空间。空间的布置与装饰极其考究，饱含着艺术色彩，更彰显出品位、个性，给人无限遐想。本案是现代中式风格的餐厅，其间"镶嵌"有诸多中国传统文化元素。中国的汉唐文化在此得以唯美地呈现，万字符号以及惟妙惟肖的鹤被巧妙运用作为空间的主题，这就赋予了鹤港料理浓郁的文化内涵，即意境，所谓"有境界，则自成高格"。营造"意境美"成为本案的关键。

本案位于东海花园会所内，为将其面积扩展，实现整个空间的通透性及互动性，设计师在空间规划上用了四根有描金的

鹤与祥云，且直通顶部的柱子，加上四面通透的水晶珠帘围成一个圆形空间，构成餐厅的视觉中心点；空间唐汉文化底蕴的丰厚决定了色彩的运用主要为紫色、绿色、金色、黑色，配以灯光，营造出独特、唯美的空间效果。

在鹤港的"内庭院"里，空气中漂浮着三文鱼的一缕清香。深色的水曲柳、马赛克地面、垂吊的珠帘、凹凸不平的文化石、源自日式生活方式的激情碰撞，无不在鹤港的每一个角落凸现、蔓延……

1. Cranes and clouds dance on the column
2. The pot flower on the round table animates this space

1．柱上有鹤与祥云共舞
2．圆桌上的鲜花让空间凭添一丝生动

Blue Brick and Ancient Charm
青砖古意

In the modern living space day and night, what we need is a place to recall the past and meet the history.
日夜处于现代化的生活空间中，我们需要一个可以缅怀过去的去处，一个可以与历史重逢的空间。

Title: Bing Huo Yuan
Designer: Yu Qingshan
Design company: Norman Design
Materials: Ps board，Rough and fired granite
Floor area: 1,200m²

项目名称: *冰火缘*
设 计 师: *余青山*
设计公司: *山川设计事务所*
主要饰材: *黑珍珠板，毛面火烧花岗岩*
建筑面积: *1200m²*

1. Blue bricks compose a massive and old space
2. The old reading lamp casts vibrant colors and breaks the coolness of the space

1. 青砖堆砌的厚重、古旧的空间
2. 老式台灯跳跃的色彩打破了空间的清冷

1. To soften the spatial compactness, the ceiling is of extremely simple style
2. Arrangement plan
3. A lobby with interplay of light and shadow

1. 为了缓和空间的紧凑感，天花运用了极其简略的设计
2. 平面布置图
3. 灯影闪烁的大厅

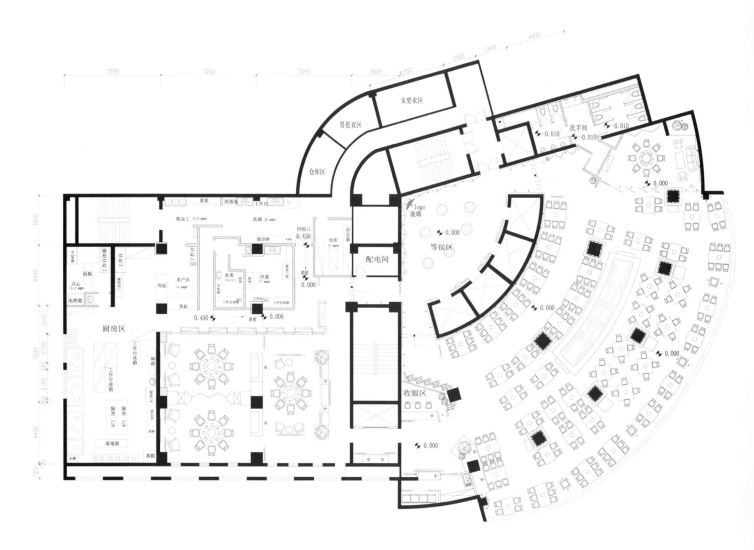

Design Concept:

The designer likes to endow the space with some compatibility. The space still has some meaningful content for people to enjoy despite the ignorance of structural layout.

The space in Bing Huo Yuan extremely shows a human-centered environment, where people can feel the warmth here and there. Here, the lighting is the designer's vocabulary. There are 365 flickering lamps for lucky waving, continuing the eternal kindness in this romantic and cozy ambience.

The entire catering space is regarded as a kind of art. The designer who is good at creating the structure to accord with the original layout, and changing the layout into structure, makes an analysis of the intrinsic spatial quality and unites the spatial functions to produce the continuous and inuous spaces. The decoration in the space is very moderate and compact, but reveals a touch of showiness and wisdom. For instance, not only the ound table in the front lobby and the red lampshade, but also the wall tructure embody this style. People can lean on the wall and rest by the able. The entire fan-shaped structure has its climax in this area. Blue

brick, stone carving, metal and cloth accessories…All the elements meet here and create a kaleidoscopic and enchanting front lobby.

The lobby of the restaurant outshines the other space. Upon entering into this area, people can see the resplendent lights and interplay of light and shadow. The lively music teems in each corner of this space, stimulates the atmosphere and allures people to come; the pond with 365 lamps for luck set off by seven lampstandards looks very magnificant, gorgeous and graceful, delivering a sense of calmness and relaxation free from vulgarity; different furniture with exotic flavor speak the strong modernity. They suggest the past, reveal the history and define the quality and cultural distinctness of this space. The entire environment boosts the modern romance, luxury, generosity and self-confience.

In this case, "kindness" is the quintessential when designing this restaurant. This well-decorated and graceful space is thoroughly created by the genuine "kindness", making each guest experience this goodwill and promote it forever. This is rightly the ultimate goal that the designer seeks for.

设计说明:

设计师喜欢让空间具有一定的包容性,让空间在剔去结构形式之后还拥有更多可以慢慢品味的内容。一个具有无穷韵味的餐饮空间会让人们像记住一道美味佳肴一样永远记住。冰火缘餐厅便是这样。

冰火缘餐厅空间极力展现人性,营造一个让人处处都能感觉到温情的世界。在这里,灯光是设计师的语言,365盏善缘信灯摇曳闪烁,一份善缘在浪漫温馨的氛围中得到永远的延续。

整个餐饮空间被构架成一种艺术,设计师善于因"势"造"式","势"改"式",剖析了固有空间特性,结合空间使用功能,实现空间连贯、迂回。空间的装饰节制、干练,却透露出张扬、智慧,如前厅的圆台、红色的灯罩、墙体的结构,无不将此贯彻。可倚墙而立,拥台而息,扇形结构在此交会,青砖、石雕、金属、布艺……所有元素在此碰撞,使充满变幻的前厅更让人着迷。

厅的大厅有众星拱月之势。进入其中，灯火绚烂，光影闪动，动感的音
充斥每个角落，激荡人心，引诱人游走其中；有365盏长明善缘灯的
池在挺立于天地之间的七根灯柱的陪伴下显得尊贵、华丽、端庄，更
一份脱离世故的气定神闲；一件件异域家具流露出浓浓的时代感，代
着过去，承载着历史，决定着空间的气质和文化特性。整个空间沐浴
大时代的浪漫、繁华、豪迈和自信。

善"为本案的精髓。有着华贵气质的精致空间，浸润着一份真挚的
善"意，每一位置身其中的客人，感受着这份"善"意，并使其永久
承。这才是设计师所追求的终极目标。

1. Exquisite VIP room
2. A confluence of antique and modern furniture
1．精致的 VIP 房
2．古式家具与现代家具的碰撞与融合

1. Front lobby
2. Bright red lampshades brighten the cool area
3. Interlaced spatial structures

1. 前厅
2. 大红的灯罩将有着冷冽质感的空间点亮
3. 交错的空间结构

1. The lamps with different heights make the dining space pure and mysterious like the church
2. Vermeil sofas are placed by the wall and lend attractions to the area
3. The vivid green adds exuberant vitality to the space
4. Just several properties can set off the gracefulness of this space
5. A place for self meditation

1．高低排列的灯让餐饮空间有教堂般的圣洁与神秘
2．鲜红色的沙发倚墙而立，不失为一道风景
3．树叶嫩绿的色彩让空间多了一份盎然的生气
4．寥寥无几的"道具"，装点出空间高贵的气质
5．一个独自冥想的去处

Myriad Twinkling Lights
万家灯火

Heading against a backflow with a unique style so as to achieve a unique view in the dining hall.
逆流而上，别样的设计理念，规划出餐饮空间别样的风景。

Title: Wan Jia Deng Huo Hotel
Designer: Song Guoliang
Design company: Ningbo Ruby Decoration Design Co.,Ltd.
Materials: Oak panel，Acrylic，Artificial euphoric stones，
Mirror stainless steel，Straw wallpaper and Ceramic tile
Floor area: 2,000m²

项目名称: 万家灯火大酒店
设 计 师: 宋国梁
设计公司: 宁波红宝石装饰设计有限公司
主要饰材: 橡木饰面板、亚克力、人造透光石、镜面不锈钢、草编墙纸、亚光砖
建筑面积: *2000m²*

1. The front hall in the evening
2\3. Stainless steel fish, droplight and screen are simple in form while rich in content

1. 夜色中的餐厅门面
2\3. 不锈钢鱼、吊灯、屏风, 形式简约, 内容丰富

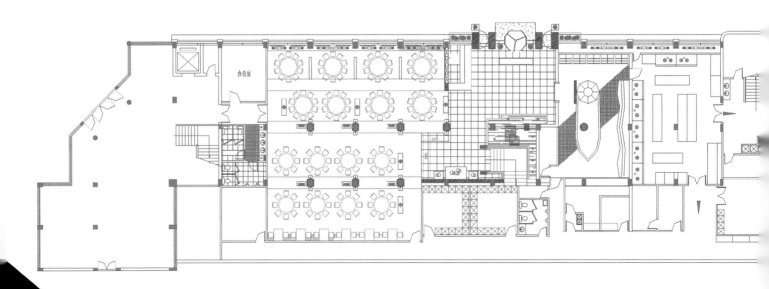

1. Traditional style is highlighted here
3. The lighting exerts a magnificent air on the space
2\4. Arrangement plan

1．传统的风格在这里得到张扬
3．灯光设计让空间极具气派
2\4．平面布置图

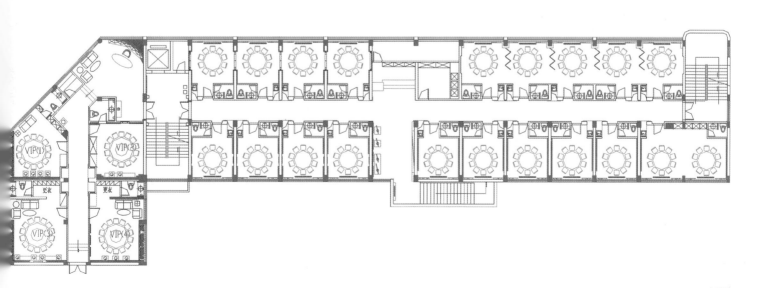

Design Concept:

When modernism and classicism come frequently to the lips of designers when brief and simple style pervades in our life, the designer makes a bold try, free from the mainstream and so called non-mainstream. Regardless of extravagance and modesty, easy and free become the goal.

It is located in Peninsula Xiangshan on the Beach of East Sea, famous for its homely dish and seafood. Through reconstruction, deficiency in appearance and function is remedied by reshaping and relocation, a more reasonable space is thus created.

The designer is aiming at a unique commercial space, florid but not showy, civil and stable, which is a mixture of luxury and brevity, purity and sophistication. Lotus leaf pattern is specially treated as an abstract object, like a continuous thread, flowing through all the space. The motif background in scarlet is conspicuous with an air of grace and dignity. National ornaments are displayed in the front show shelf, abundant in variety, such as flower arrangement and jewelry box. The hall is dominated by a series of black and-white photographs and lighting fixtures. Listening to the fall of water and gazing into the ruffle of the water is a sort of entertainment. The stair is creatively designed, handling the shades of color and light skillfully, while the high space takes on a vivid look. The point and line seem to dance with musical notes delightfully. A fine spectacle is created by virtue of glimmering platform and candles, dreamy and misty. The designer is trying to express fully the details of this space, working out all the potential beauty, from which partial perfection is enchanting.

设计说明:

当现代主义和复古主义还是设计师谈论的话题的时候, 当简约风尚和极简主义倍受推崇的时候, 设计师在这里做了一次逆流而上的尝试, 放弃所有的观点和批判, 收起所谓的主流和非主流, 形式夸张了, 含蓄了不必在意, 让随心所欲成为主体。

万家灯火大酒店坐落于东海之滨的象山半岛, 以家常菜和海味而闻名。这个项目通过改造而成, 删除了改造前功能和美学上的缺憾, 进行新的定位和重塑, 让空间组合更为合理。

设计师力求营造一个个性、人文、张扬而又不失沉稳的商业空间, 空间实现奢华与纯朴的揉捏, 迷幻与纯净的交织。这一实现过程是设计师对空间充分把握的体现。荷叶图形处理成抽象形式, 游走于各空间, 像一条不断的线; 醒目的大幅主题背景与猩红色调透出雍容典雅, 前面的展示区堆叠着民族饰品——仿古手饰盒、小动物、非原雕、现代陶艺, 不必在意谁更精彩; 大厅里夸张的灯饰, 仿古的壁, 反映本土风情的黑白照片, 精致的插花成为这里的主宰; 在曲折有趣的水景区边听潺潺流水, 看荡漾的花瓣也别有一番情趣; 具有想像力的主楼梯间刻意把握了形式的主体感和光与影的变化, 高挑的空间具有动感的造型, 点与线像跳跃的音符在飞舞, 由抽象的艺术装置和立体结构构成; 发光的台阶, 延伸的烛光, 迷离飘渺似梦幻中的仙境, 成就一个唯美的视角; 二楼过厅的不锈钢鱼, 来自于一个著名雕塑家; 镜面不锈钢的质地折射着灯光和环境的变幻, 鲜活的色彩在流动。设计师想要在这一空间里留住和表达所有的细节和小品, 挖掘潜在式美的潜力, 编织着矛盾并营造了和谐, 细节的完美更让人心醉。

1		3
2		4	5

1\2. Assorted national accessories add more flavor to the space
3. The motif background and ornaments are conspicuous with an air of grace and dignity
4. Fine chinaware and bundles of flowers decorate the table gracefully
5. Grace of classic lighting fixtures

1 \ 2．各具特色的民族饰品为空间增添更多风情
3．猩红色调的大幅背景图与陈设的饰品尽显雍容与华贵
4．精致的陶器与成束的花朵是餐桌上的优雅点缀
5．形态优雅的古典灯饰

1. Beauty of candle-light
2\6. Decoration details
3. Reception desk at the entrance
4. A romance of ascending step by step is created by the glimmering candles
5. Classic combination of white and black, red and black
7. The decorative accessories match well enough

1．烛光之美
2\6．装饰细节
3．餐厅入口的接待台
4．点点烛光营造拾阶而上的浪漫
5．黑与白的经典，红与黑的经典
7．饰物的搭配亦是如此的恰如其分

Cultural Source
文化本源

With dozens of symbols, the dining space turns out to be a
valuable dictionary for seeking cultural source.
各种象征性符号的拼贴，让餐饮空间同时成为一本供人了解和探索文化本
源的"宝典"。

Title: Gancaixuan Restaurant
Designer: Jiang Tianlun
Design company: Office of Designer Jiang Tianlun
Materials: Marble，Imported Printing ink，
Mirrors，Steel, Imported carpet.
Floor area: 3,000m²

项目名称：赣彩轩酒楼
设 计 师：江天伦
设计公司：深圳江天伦设计师事务所
主要饰材：大理石、进口油墨、茶镜、沙钢、进口地毯
建筑面积：3000m²

	2
1	3

1. Chinese-style entrance
2\3. Smooth and elegant curves on graceful stairs
1．中式风格的酒楼入口
2＼3．轻盈的楼梯有着流畅而优美的曲线

Design Concept:

In this case, based on his own understanding of the Gan culture, the designer uses skillful techniques to achieve a special effect, creating a perfect atmosphere for dining and meanwhile embracing the cultural essence, similar to the Chinese couplets: amounting the square hall, savoring the essence of culture; holding the glass, appreciating the smell of wine and food.

As for the structure, the designer integrates three elements harmoniously, modern simple decorative methods, Chinese traditional abstract expression and modern exquisite decorative materials. No matter passage or stair, straight line or curve, the implicit decoration on them is distinctive: the whole space is divided into many different small ones with their own styles and assorted descriptions, in which neither fashion nor function is ignored. It is impressively rich in a wide range of view since the spaces are all connected to the outside scenery. The whole space embodies a style of cultural sediment, transferring visibility into invisibility skillfully.

The designer artfully chose 11 famous cities all of which have long history of civilization so as to express the content of the space. Skilled techniques give vent to all kinds of classic Gan cultures and make them accessible from

tradition to modern, such as ancient seal. The fabulous sight couched poems:"the lone geese flying against the grand sunset, the autum water melting into the far—off sky" is recapitulated here. Teng Monar Pavilion and Academy in Nanchang; Peach blossom and Mountain Lu Jiujiang; copper in Shangrao; local facial makeup in operas in Yiyar Kejia circumjacent house, suona horn, rice; coal and dancing patterns Pingxiang; firecrackers and former residence in Yichun; china and comme cave in Jingde Town ,the list can go on and on··· No need of long journe no need of waiting, you can enjoy them heartily. How pleasant!

Part of the civilization carriers here are enlarged or recombined in co effect. Various bright hues are flowing freely, leaving a strong visual impa and acting out people's imagination, which meanwhile plays a part one of the links in the hotel space. Besides, select and elaborate patter produce a sort of abstract appeal.

This kind of work is endowed with a new mission, that is, it explains t source of Gan civilization intensively and takes the lead for the culture.

1. Tidy and orderly arrangement of the dining hall
2. Assorted elements such as ceiling, columns, and wallboard are eye-dazzling in the light
3. The red wall makes the restaurant more active
4. The chinaware hung overhead is another sight of culture

1．餐厅布置错落有致
2．天花、柱体、墙面饱含的诸多设计元素足以让人眼花缭乱
3．置于半空的陶瓷是空间的又一文化看点
4．红色墙体的点缀让餐厅更具活跃的气氛

1. Circles
2. A sight in the entrance of stairs
3. Aisle
4. The corridor also shows culture

1．圆
2．楼梯口的"风光"
3．走道
4．走道也成为展示文化的长廊

1. The service desk is drenched with ancient Chinese cultu
2. Sumptuous passage
3. The umbrellas hung upside down on the ceiling add to a tra
of romance

1．中国古文化浸润的服务台
2．豪华走道
3．天花上倒挂的红伞给空间增添一丝浪漫

设计说明：

本案中设计师凭着自己对赣文化的独特理解，运用娴熟的室内设计技法，成功演绎出"登堂入室，尺寸方圆，即可揽胜佳文化；执箸举觞，梅兰竹菊，唯真留香赣彩轩"的餐饮文化空间。

在空间结构形式上，设计师实现了现代简约的装饰技法、中国传统抽象的物质表征元素与现代高品味装饰材料的和谐统一。无论是过道、楼梯、直线或曲线，还是门窗桌椅或饰品，不着痕迹的曲折和错位形成了自己的特点：空间被分割成不同小天地，结构各具风格，景象万千，功能与时尚相结合且相互包容的每个小空间又由或朦胧或通透的细部结构衔接等等，营造了丰富的视角，人行其间，移步换景，江南风情尽显眼底。总体空间着力沉淀风格，化有形为无形。

在空间内容表现上，设计师巧妙地选择了11个能够集中彰显赣文化特色的历史文化名城，组成一个餐饮文化空间，运用高超的装饰技术将千年来各种厚重、经典的赣文化本原载体纳入具体行为，化传统的

意象文化为可视听的装饰文化。比如，古印鉴；千古绝唱——"落霞与孤鹜齐飞，秋水共长天一色"的风物重现；南昌的滕王阁、书院，九江的桃花源、庐山；上饶的铜矿、弋阳地方戏剧脸谱；赣州的客家围屋、唢呐、水稻；萍乡的煤、傩舞图案；宜春的鞭炮、明清民居；景德镇的陶瓷、古代制陶民窑……不必远行，不必等待，大快朵颐之际，即可默味春秋，岂不快哉！

在这里，部分文化载体的色调或构成被放大或重新组合，各种鲜艳流动的色彩及造型给人带来强烈的视觉冲击，在整体氛围中让人更具想像力，成为酒楼空间连贯的纽带之一。精心挑选、制作的条纹图案直接、简练、富有抽象的感染力。

这部近似构成主义的作品被赋予新的使命，即集中诠释赣文化的本源，并引领之。

1. Washing room is a classic combination of tradition and modern
2. Washing room possesses heavy historical and cultural aura
3. 3rd floor arrangement plan
4. 2nd floor arrangement plan
5. 1st floor arrangement plan

1. 洗手间是传统与现代组合的经典
2. 洗手间具有浓厚的历史感及文化气息
3. 三层平面布置图
4. 二层平面布置图
5. 一层平面布置图

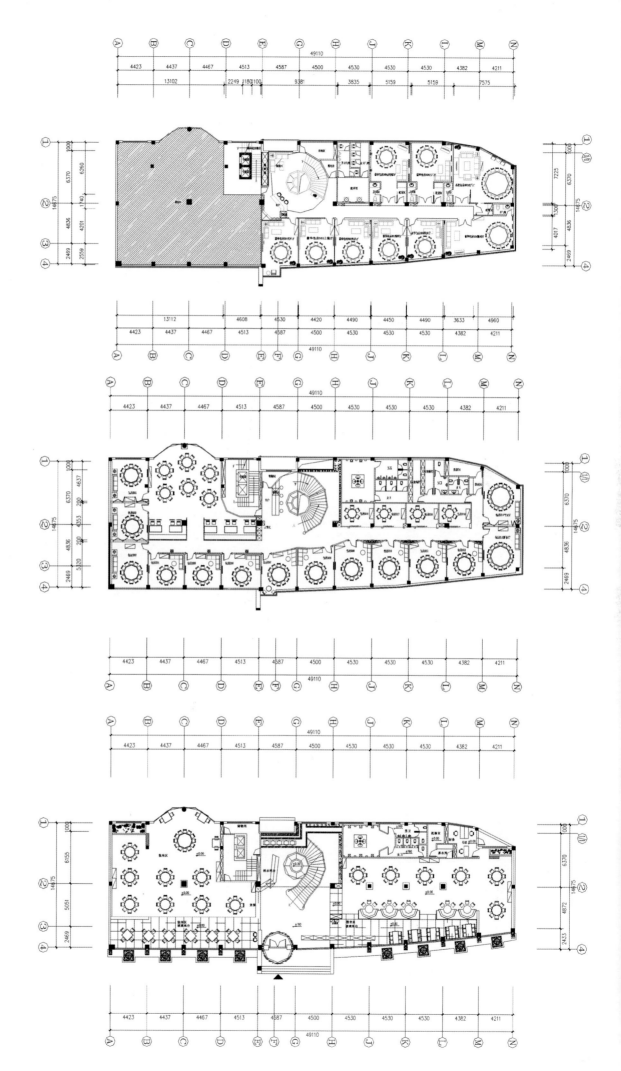

	2	3
1	4	5
	6	7

1\2\3\4\5. Separate VIP rooms with distinctive decorations represent the appeals and charms of various cultures

6\7. Decoration details

1\2\3\4\5. 不同特色装饰的VIP房，让人感受到多种文化的韵味与魅力

6\7. 装饰细节

1. Exterior of the hotel among lights
2. A half-open VIP room enclosed by stainless steel tubes
3. The lone geese flying against the grand sunset, the autumn water melting into the far-off sky
4. Chinese culture is well expressed in the door of VIP rooms
5. Ancient window lattice and modern dinning arrangement in the same space are in no conflict

1．灯火掩映中的酒楼外观
2．用不锈钢管围合而成的半开放VIP房
3．落霞与孤鹜齐飞，秋水共长天一色
4．VIP房门的设计渗透着中国文化
5．古式窗棂与充满现代感的餐位布置在同一空间并不见冲突

Japanese Style

日式风格

Natural Ambience
自然境界

Catering is a kind of culture. So dining space is not just a space but an effective carrier of culture.

餐饮，是一种文化。餐饮空间，就不能只是一个空间，它更应该是一种文化的有力载体。

Title: Jinben Restaurant
Designer: Zhuang Xiancheng
Design company: Guangzhou Xuzhuang Decoration and
Design Co.,Ltd.
Materials: Baking surface Fujian syenite, Imported
black galaxy，Natural surface Fujian syenite,
White cobblestone，Withered tree，White Latex
paint，Makore wooden facing
Floor area: 2,800m²

项目名称：金本餐厅
设 计 师：庄仙程
设计公司：广州市徐庄装饰设计有限公司
主要饰材：火烧面福建黑花岗石、进口黑金沙、自然面福建黑花
岗石、白色鹅卵石、枯树、白色乳胶漆、麦哥梨木饰面板
建筑面积：2800m²

1. The creation of restaurant's ambience begins at the entrance
2. The space has warm colors
3. These two exquisite crystal pendant lamps gracefully glorify the space

1．餐厅氛围的营造从入口开始
2．空间有一抹底色，就叫温暖
3．两盏精美的水晶吊灯将空间点缀得富丽堂皇

Design Concept:

Jinben Restaurant is a Japanese–style restaurant, in which the Japanese interior design elements can be seen everywhere. There are two functional parts in the restaurant, the western restaurant and the Taiwan Shuanshuanguo, which determine some separate areas in space. When partitioning different areas, the designer rearranges the spatial circulation and mostly adopts the virtual space as the designing technique.

The designer did the survey in the site and found problems with the long depth before conceiving this project. So shortening the depth becomes the principle design concept of the hall of this restaurant, which occupies an area nearly 100m² . The planar design of restaurant is from the water wall at the entrance, to the central thatching via the lotus pond water feature, creating an integrated area on the whole. The restaurant includes the large halls and the small halls, while the VIP rooms are set outside the halls. The scattered tables and seats for people to have beefsteak are suitably placed in a large–scale and unbroken space, which functions as a buffet dinner area. In addition, there are another two buffet dinner tables in the front and back areas of the restaurant. There is a bar in the west section (the place for having beefsteak) and an optical fiber wall in the fire protection area.

1. There is a confluence of the most primitive straw and the high-tech optical fiber. Surrounded by water, the straw mattress as seat evokes the pleasure when people have meals in this restaurant
2. Under the thatching, when listening to the rippling flowing water, you can feel a return to the primitive environment

1. 最原始的稻草与高科技的光纤同在，四周环水，拔地而起的榻榻米设计使涮涮锅的用餐充满了乐趣
2. 茅草屋下，流水潺潺，原滋原味的空间环境让你有回归自然的体验

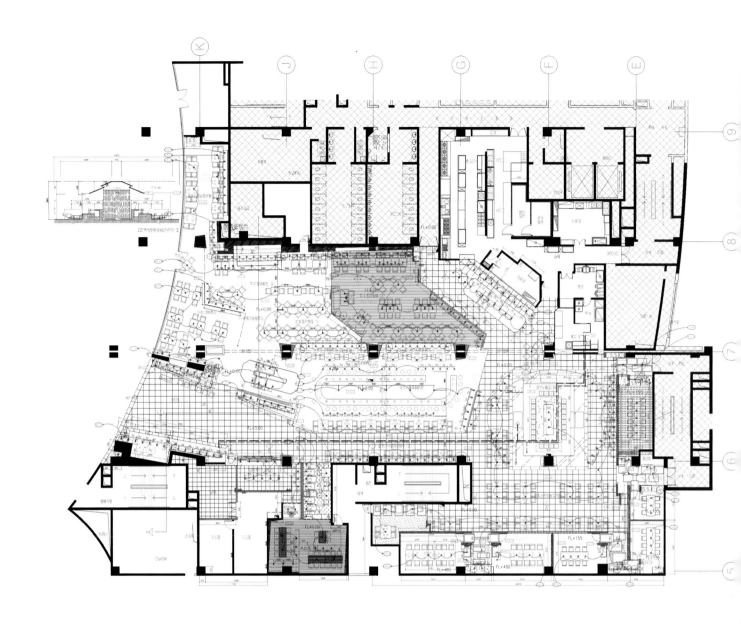

The spatial materials in this case have their separate themes, ...lly shaping contrast, giving certain visual impact to people ...d showing their spatial identity. For example, there are ...ntrasts between the thick baking surface Fujian syenite ...boring and the polished imported linoleum flooring, the ...ick baking surface black galaxy table and the natural ...urface table. A high-tech optical fiber wall under the ...xtremely primitive thatching even makes vivid contrast ...etween the primitiveness and modernity.

...ost of the sections in the restaurant don't adopt the ...ommonplace square patterns but instead use the radiate ...yout to show the concentrated expressive force. In addition, ...e yellow man-made sandstone with harvest flavor, the ...eclining water wall, flowing water wall, thick baking surface ...ujian syenite wall not only achieve the sharp contrast in ...aterials but also arouse the charm of the space, which ...mulate people to enter the interior space when they stand ...tside.

...e designer makes some exclusive designs in each area of ...e restaurant. For instance, there is a crystal wine rack on ...e natural seat stone in the hall. Shuanshuaguo bar has the ...range umbrella-shaped lamps, and it boasts a thatching ...ntrally located in the area that evokes the rural flavor. The ...ecial performance of the perforated wooden columns and ...e irregular huge wooden facing columns breaks the silence ...the space and animates the entire area.

1. Arrangement plan
2. Curtain of fiber marks off two dinning area of different content
3. This area has the strongest Japanese flavor
4. The partition design is very charming

1 . 平面布置图
2 . 光纤垂帘划分出不同内容的两个餐饮区域
3 . 东洋风味浓郁的区域
4 . 隔断的设计具有无限风情

设计说明:

金本餐厅是属于东洋风格设计的餐厅，其间日式室内设计的元素随处可见。餐厅有两部分的功能，即西餐和台湾涮涮锅。餐厅的功能决定了餐厅在空间上会有一定的区域划分，设计师在划分区域时，打乱了空间路线，采用了虚拟空间的设计手法。

在本案构思之前，设计师考察现场时发现场地的进深过大，因此就把将进深拉近作为了餐厅近百平方米的大厅设计的指导理念。餐厅的平面规划是从门口的水幕墙开始的，然后到荷花池水景，再到中心地带的茅草屋，形成一个整体。餐厅中包括了大厅空间和小厅空间，VIP 房的空间设置在大厅之外，大面积平整的空间里恰到好处地设置了牛排散座。这是一个半自助餐厅，因此，还在餐厅前后设置了两个自助餐台。在牛排西餐部分有水吧的设置，在消防分区用了光纤幕墙设计。

本案在空间材料的使用上有其自身的特色，即充分地让使用材质形成对比，从而给人一定的视觉刺激，突出空间个性。如粗面火烧面的福建黑花岗石地面与光泽的进口亚麻地板、粗面火烧面的黑金沙花岗台面与自然面的台面侧边形成对比。非常具有原始意味的稻草屋下高科技的光纤幕墙设计，更是原始与现代的鲜明对比。

餐厅的大厅部分打破了普遍的方正设计模式，使用富有集合力的射设计。富有收获感觉的黄色合成沙岩、倾斜墙面中的水幕墙、流水面、粗面火烧面的福建黑花岗石斜墙等，除了形成强烈的材质对比外还让空间透露着一种吸引力，使人在餐厅外面就有想进入空间内部冲动。

设计师在餐厅的每个区域都保持了一些独特的设计，如大厅里给人然感觉的石墩上有晶莹通透的红酒架，涮涮锅吧有造型怪异的伞状型的"灯"。最有特色的是中心区域的茅草屋，足以给人野外的气息还有半通透设计的木柱及不规则的木饰面大柱子，这些独特的存在破了空间的沉默，让整个空间活跃起来。

	2
1	
	3

1. The high elliptic dining table and the high chairs constitute a unique dining area in the restaurant
2. Small lobby
3. There are two distinct dining table arrangements in the lobby

1．高高的椭圆形餐台与高脚椅组成餐厅中一个独特的就餐区
2．雅致的小厅空间
3．大厅中两种不同的餐桌布置方式

The Story of Nature
自然物语

There is no doubt that the Japanese spatial designs pay special respect to nature. The designer breaks the spatial limits and creates a natural environment for people to experience life.

日式空间设计对自然的崇尚是无可比拟的——突破空间的限制，体验自然，品味原味人生。

Title: He Ting Japanese Cooking
Designer: Liu Jie
Materials: Paint, Ironwork, Aluminum grating, Wooden floor
Floor area: 600㎡

项目名称: *和亭日本料理*
设 计 师: 刘杰
主要饰材: 涂料、铁艺、铝格栅、木地板
建筑面积: *600㎡*

1. The walls on both sides of the aisle shape the contrast between roughness and smoothness
2. The restaurant in the dark is more attractive and charming
3. The floor-to-ceiling window infinitely extends the space and makes a capacious environment

1．走道两边的墙面形成了粗糙与光滑的对比
2．夜色中的餐厅深邃、迷人，更具魅力
3．落地窗让空间得到无限的延伸，显得开阔

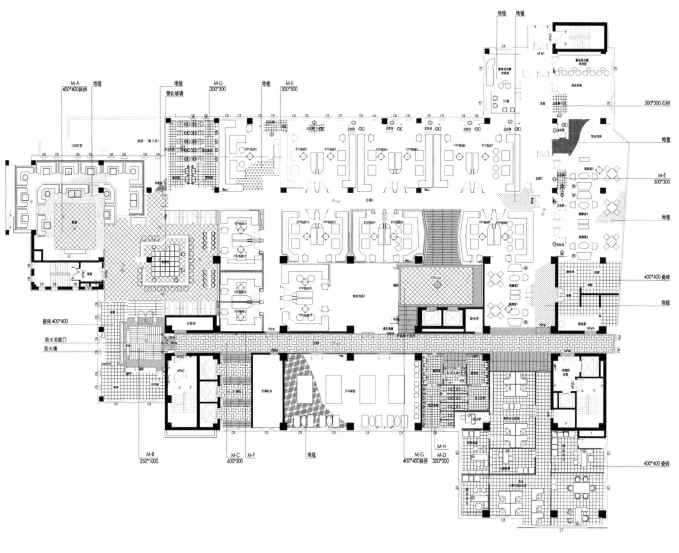

1. 3rd floor arrangement plan
2. Arrangement plan
3. Various window shapes can create different interior ambien

1．三层平面布置图
2．平面布置图
3．不同的窗户形式让室内氛围有很大的不同

esign Concept:

e design of He Ting Japanese Cooking derives from the nature. It is the ture that enlightens the designer's desire. The designer brings the tural elements into design, which blazons forth the design concept of alth and simplicity. Being a Japanese cooking store, Japanese elements e taken into use a lot. Besides the overall layout that intimates Japanese staurants, the decoration adds a lot to the Japanese style in the space.

ere is a corridor made of stainless steel that intimates the bamboo ves and walls of coarse machine planed stones, which form natural enery indoors by the modern materials. The Sushi Bar takes the light– nsmitted wall, which is created by the combination of wood veins and ss, as its background. The background of the eye–catching large ss–relief oak "Wave Wall" is a very characteristic design in this taurant, which expresses flow and movement in a manner of etness. The fantastic lighting effect is another focus, which is de of metal line frames covered with fibers. It is just like the

interesting "bird's nest", also like "a cage to catch the shrimp", giving off amber rays of light to lighten the space. This kind of lighting design not only brings the natural flavor, but also makes the space quite gentle. The folding screen of ironwork with traditional Japanese patterns separates the Barbeque Area from the Dinning Area, which gives a secret feeling and enables these two areas to glance at each other simultaneously. This design unwittingly shows the designer's originality and doesn't stick to one pattern.

Many kinds of materials are used in this restaurant, and different materials can achieve diverse spatial effects. Therefore, the space not only possesses both cool and cozy parts, which makes the atmosphere exchange and minglement come true. He Ting Japanese Cooking is one of the most advanced and perfect annotation to the art space.

1. A screen decorated by Japanese traditional patterns
2. Materials reflect the simplicity style
3. This warm space full of graceful artistic conception makes an effort to create the peaceful atmosphere

1．具有日本传统图案的屏风
2．现代材质铺就的极简主义路线
3．具有优美意境的暖意空间，着力表现静谧之气

1. The bird's nest-style droplight is the focal point in this case
2. Restaurant
3. This place is a modern art space instead of a restaurant

1．"鸟巢"式吊灯的设计是本案的焦点
2．餐厅一隅
3．仿佛不是餐厅，而是时尚的艺术空间

设计说明：

和亭日本料理的设计灵感来源于自然界，自然界激发了设计师的创作欲，将自然的元素引入室内空间，宣扬健康、淳朴的设计理念。既然是日本料理店，日式元素在此得到大肆的运用，除了整体布局对日式餐厅进行模拟外，在装饰上也给日式风格做了很好的补充。

空间内有不锈钢做成的仿竹林走廊及粗矿机刨石的墙，用现代的材料在室内塑造自然风景。寿司吧以由木纹与玻璃结合所呈现的透光墙面为背景。用橡木做的大型浅浮雕"波浪墙"背景非常引人注目，它以一种安静的方式表现漂移和游动，是餐厅内个性十足的设计。奇异的灯光效果，成为空间的又一看点，它是由纤维包裹的金属线架制作的

灯笼，恰似有趣的"鸟巢"，又似"捕虾的笼子"，散发出琥珀色光将空间点亮，这类灯光设计既将自然的风情带入餐厅，又使空间更柔和感。有日本传统图案的铁艺屏风把烧烤区和就餐区分开，产生种隐秘的感觉，但同时使两个区域可以相互窥望，不经意间流露出计师的不拘一格、独具匠心。

多种材质在餐厅得到运用，不同的材质能取得不同的空间效果，此，空间既具有清冷的部分，又有温馨的板块，实现了空间气氛互交融。和亭日本料理餐厅，是对最前卫的艺术空间的完美诠释。

1

1. Oak bass-relief feature wall blends into the entire space
1．橡木的浅浮雕背景墙和整个空间融为一体

Modern Japanese Style
现代和风

Concision, neatness, brevity, moderation , profundity···an inseparable link between the Japanese style and these vocabulary.

凝练、工整、简洁、节制、深邃⋯⋯现代日式风格空间的设计无法与这些词汇脱离。

Title: Renqing
Designers: NORIO OGAWA,CHIKARA SASAKI,SHINICHIRO YOKOI
Design company: Shanghai Infix Design Consulting Co,Ltd.
Materials: Strengthened glass，Emulsion paint，Bricks,
Marble，Oak timber
Floor area: 296㎡

项目名称: 仁清
设 计 师: 小川训央、佐佐木力、横井慎一郎
设计公司: 上海英菲柯斯设计咨询有限公司
主要饰材: 钢化玻璃、乳胶漆、砖块、大理石、橡木
建筑面积: *296㎡*

1. The entrance lays foundation for the theme of the entire room
2. The droplights of the floor set at different levels are a bright spot
3. The floor of the passage is paved with natural stones

1．餐厅入口处玄关的设计奠定了整个餐厅的氛围基调
2．一楼酒水吧台高低分布的吊灯组合无疑是餐厅的亮点
3．走道地面由天然石材铺就而成

Design Concept:

The shop is located at Nanchang Road, Shanghai—another birthplace of ancient architecture and famous for its tranquility and beauty. Different from Bund and New Universe which are both famous for clamor, here, you can breathe the long-awaiting fresh air.

Walking on Nanchang Road, you are greeted by the rough lines which are the eye-catching feature of Renqing.

Leaning against the U-shaped service desk on the first floor, you can relish the glass bottles set among the light and savor Japanese style colorless spirit as you like. Strolling up to the second floor, the 14-meter wide wall is the bright spot of the shop. The second floor has both open chatting bar and independent rooms in every size which can satisfy various needs of customers.

This is a game between timber, stone and steel. Sojourning in the space which is saturated with sunshine and abundant natural materials, sipping the Japanese style colorless spirit which is brewed carefully and blends with the fresh food suitably, the customers are surely to be enchanted with the excellent "Renqing Cuisine". You will experience a sort of "Modern Japanese Fashion" peculiar in the nationality.

1	2
	3
	4

1. The simple decoration and design on the second floor makes the space more grand and comfortable
2. A round look of the inside
3. 2nd floor arrangement plan
4. 1st floor arrangement plan

1 . 二楼沙龙区简约的设计装饰让空间更显大方、舒适
2 . 环视沙龙内部
3 . 二层平面布置图
4 . 一层平面布置图

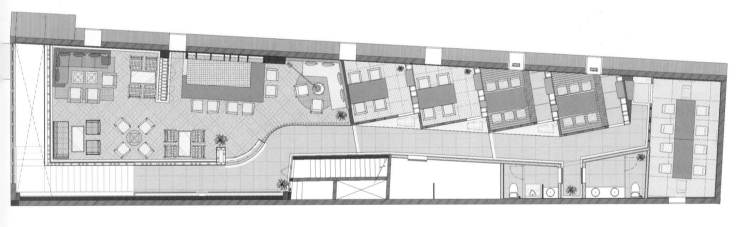

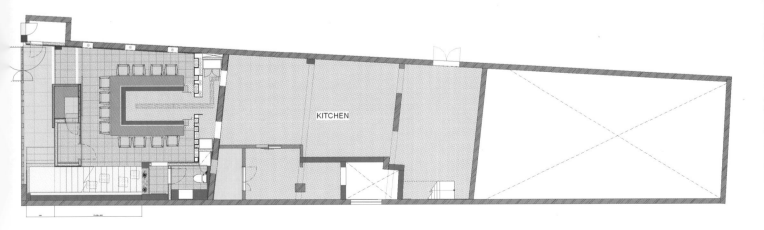

KITCHEN

1. The salon entrance and wall
2. The passage of VIP room
3. The entrance of the salon on the second floor

1．从沙龙后半部看到的沙龙入口处与流水墙
2．进入VIP房的走廊
3．二楼沙龙的入口部分

1\2. The color and texture of metallic stairs echo to the wall
3. The service desk in the restaurant

1 \ 2．简易金属楼梯的色泽、质感与墙体相呼应

3．餐厅服务台

设计说明：

我们的主题店铺，坐落在老式建筑的又一发源地——上海南昌路、一个以美丽幽静著称的地方。不同于外滩、新天地的喧闹，在这里你能呼吸到一种久别的空气。

走在南昌路上，眼前浮现出的粗线条，就是惹眼的"仁清"。

依靠在一楼，呈大大"U"字形的吧台边，随意欣赏着被若有若无的灯光环抱的玻璃瓶，尽情品味着日式烧酒的余温。踱步到二楼，与楼梯相连达 14 米之宽的流水墙是小店的点睛之笔。集开放式聊天吧、大小包间于一体的二楼能满足来客各式各样的空间利用需求。

这是一场木、石、铁的游戏。陶醉在这个浸透了阳光，充满大自然气息的空间，品味着被精心酝酿，并搭配了合宜的新鲜食物的日式纯色精神，顾客一定会为这种绝妙的"仁清烹调"而着迷。在这里你将体验一种日本特有的——"现代和风"。

Southeast Asian Style

①.Banana Leaf Curry House
蕉叶咖喱屋餐厅

②.Mingtien Coffee Language (Dream Town Branch)
名典咖啡语茶（万科城分店）

Deep Courtyard
庭院深深

"Deep, deep the courtyard where he is, so deep. It is veiled by smoke-like willows heap on heap. By curtain on curtain and screen on screen". The dining space with strong tropical flavor is infinitely expanded here representing the profound artistic conception of courtyard.
"庭院深深深几许？杨柳堆烟，帘幕无重数。"热带风情浓郁的餐饮空间无限延伸，重现庭院深锁的意境美。

Title: Banana Leaf Curry House
Designer: He Yongming
Design company: He Yongming Design Studio
Materials: Dry bamboo，Fir board，Artificial tree，Salmon pink (ICI)
Floor area: 960m²

项目名称： 蕉叶咖喱屋餐厅
设 计 师： 何永明
设计公司： 何永明设计师工作室
主要饰材： 干竹、杉木板、人造树木、橙红色(ICI)
建筑面积： 960m²

	2	
1		3

1. Elegant and generous bar table
2. Restaurant entrance
3. People can see the exquisite views in the lobby via the aisle

1．精致而大气的吧台
2．餐厅入口
3．穿过走道，可以看到大厅中的另外一番景致

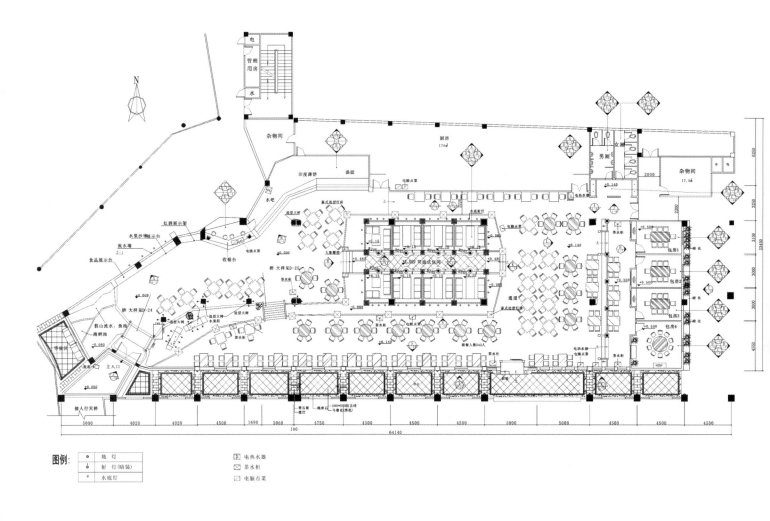

图例:
- ⊙ 地 灯
- ⚙ 射 灯(暗装)
- ✦ 水底灯

- ⊠ 电热水器
- ⊠ 茶水柜
- ▨ 电脑点菜

Design Concept:

Banana Leaf Curry House is another beachhead o the Hong Kong Banana Leaf Group that tries t develop its chain store.

In this space, the designer would like to create dinning space with strong Southeast Asian flave through the combination of South Asian style an the conception of operators as well as the buildir features.

Banana Leaf Curry House lies in the prosperou area of the pedestrian street, with lifelike coppe elephant sculpture, slate pedestal and dry bambo ceiling. These decorations play an important ro as the transition before people are led to the spac with South Asian atmosphere. The corrido passage from entrance to the restaurant is als full of exoticism taste. The entrance and passag enable the customers to transit from the crowe and busy pedestrian street to an interior spac that is filled with South Asian taste, thereb possessing a relax and quiet mind.

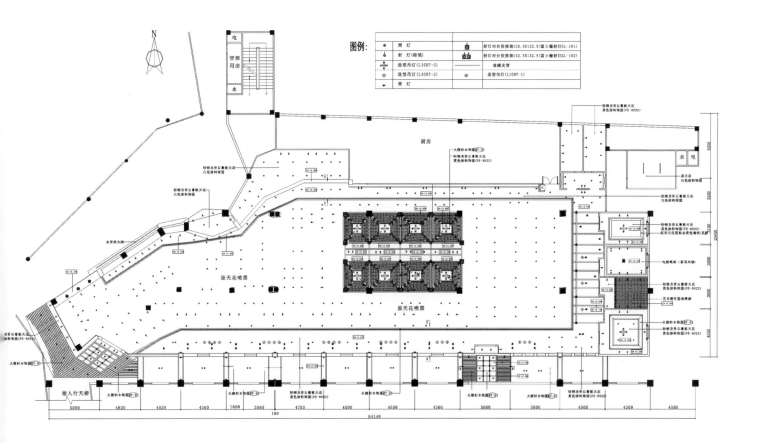

图例:
⊕ 筒 灯	🏮 射灯对台位按装132.5X132.5(富士射灯GL-101)
⊕ 射 灯(暗筒)	🏮 射灯对台位按装132.5X132.5(富士射灯GL-102)
✛ 造型吊灯(LIGHT-3)	── 暗藏光管
⊕ 造型吊灯(LIGHT-2)	⊕ 造型吊灯(LIGHT-1)
⊕ 壁 灯	

电
管理用房
水

厨房

水 电

1	3
2	4

1. Arrangement plan
2. The long aisle seemingly looks endless
3. Plan of ceiling
4. The lighting and materials announce the inherent qualities of this restaurant—nature and harmony

1．平面布置图
2．悠长的走道，看不到尽头
3．天花平面布置图
4．灯光和材质体现出餐厅自然和谐的本色

177

The restaurant operator always takes the tropical taste as the image axis, and in this cas the designer uses a great deal of contrast of dry bamboo, fir board, rough cement sa plaster, salmon pink (ICI) and artificial tree, which displays an enchanting and ravishi tropical garden scenery and gives natural and comfortable enjoy in vision.

Every design of the restaurant has its own purpose. For example, a group of tropical fo display cases are set on the left of the entrance, which can catch customers' attention, a another scenery and give directions to customers. Black is the color of the ceiling, which forr the spatial effect to stretch upwards, and gives the feeling of looking from a high place; main passage is topped with artificial trees and leaves, which conveys a warm and frien atmosphere to welcome guests.

this case, there are many irregular columns, which is the most important element in
affecting the beauty and order of the space, however, the partially opened seat area
solves this problem perfectly.

Many kinds of pierced decoration methods are used in this design, which becomes
another appreciation focus. Separated by the pierced wooden lattice, the bamboo
screen not only divides this area but also enriches the spatial layers; the compartment
separated by the fir board forms a secret dining space, and together with the distinctive
grille, this makes it possible to communicate through the interior activities in the
compartment.

1. A feast under the shade
1."绿阴"下的一场盛宴

设计说明：

蕉叶咖喱屋餐厅是香港蕉叶集团发展蕉叶咖喱屋连锁版图的又一据点。

在这个空间里，设计师希望透过东南亚风格结合经营者的理念和建筑本身的特点，打造出具有浓厚东南亚特色的餐饮空间。

餐厅位于步行街的繁华地段，餐厅入口处有栩栩如生的铜象、板岩石座，还有干竹编织的天花，这些装饰在将人引入东南亚风情的空间之前起到了过渡作用。从入口进入餐厅的走道亦被营造成具有异国情调的空间氛围。入口和通道让顾客从餐厅外喧嚣的步行街环境转换至充满东南亚风情的室内环境中，心境变得悠然、宁静。

餐厅的经营者向来以热带风情作为形象主轴，设计师就在本案设计中大量运用干竹、杉木板、粗面水泥、橙红色（ICI）、人造树木作对比，呈现一片令人迷醉的热带园林景观，给人以自然、舒适的视觉享受。

餐厅每一处的设计都别具用意。如入口处左侧设置的一组热带特色物展示柜，既让空间多了一道风景，又指点了顾客的消费；餐厅天板选配黑色，形成空间向上延伸的效果，给人高挑的视觉感受；全厅的主路线两旁铺制了人造树和树叶，传达出亲切热情的迎宾气氛。

本案的柱体较多，而且不规整，是影响空间美观与整齐的最大因素，开放式坐位区的设置使这一难题得到完美的解决。

设计师在设计中运用了多种镂空造型手法，成为餐厅另一个观赏焦，镂空的木格隔间、竹帘屏风在分割区域的同时让空间的层次丰富来；由杉木板间隔出来的包房，形成一个私密的用餐空间，搭配上色的格子窗，让包房内外产生交流的可能。

1. Complicated spatial layout and the featured decorations make each space interesting
2. This is an unostentatious, artless and comfortable semi-open compartment
3. The cabin-shaped lamps concentrate the Southeast Asian flavor.
4. Detailed landscape in the restaurant

1．复杂的空间结构，特色的装饰让每一处空间都充满趣味
2．朴素、自然、舒适的半开放式包房
3．小屋造型的灯具是东南亚风情的浓缩
4．餐厅细部景观

1. In the dim light, the artificial scenery is vividly set off
2. The exhibiting cabinet of tropical featured plants

1．朦胧的灯光下，人造的景物也显得格外生动
2．热带特色植物的展示柜

Preserve Original Taste
典藏原味

Return is a warm word. This is a space returns to a natural and original environment. Do you feel consideration and kindness in this ambience?

回归，是一个温暖的词汇。一个回归自然原味的空间，是否能让您拥有更加体贴、亲切的感觉？

Title：Mingtien Coffee Language (Dream Town Branch)
Designers: Liang Jingquan, Shi Lin
Design company: Shenzhen Mincillier Furniture & Decoration Design Co., Ltd.
Materials: Stone, Timber, Glass
Floor area: 220m²

项目名称：名典咖啡语茶（万科城分店）
设 计 师：梁景泉，史琳
设计公司：深圳市名斯利烨家具·装饰设计有限公司
主要饰材：石材、木材、玻璃
建筑面积：220m²

1. The corner of the restaurant is full of emotional appeal
2. The bright yellow wall adds the fresh and natural flavor into this space
3. This wooden wine cabinet functions as a pragmatic and beautiful partition

1. 餐厅的一角亦被营造得很有情调
2. 明黄色的墙面让空间充满清新自然的气息
3. 木质的酒柜充当隔断，实用又美观

Design Concept:

Any spatial design should blend in well with the surrounding background. When the Mingtien Coffee Language which is well-known for its classical preservation of coffee flavor was settled in the Dream Town, the designer has considered this idea. The architectural designs of Dream Town pay much attention to the natural and cultural context of the site and also attach importance to the close relation between human and nature. On one hand, the designs harmoniously tone with the entire building style, while on the other hand, they respond to the casual and bright image of the western coffee restaurant that leaves the impression on our minds. The designs fully reflect the natural and harmonious themes. The designer creates a unique catering space full of strong Bali Island flavor here.

In this case, the relaxed designs are the main concepts. The restaurant is mainly decorated by bright yellow and the wood color as the tone and employs a lot of natural materials such as stone and timber so as to skillfully infuse the natural elements into the designs. The renovated shop front adopts the large-scale glass, which enables the light to freely penetrate the interior spaces to present the pleasing and natural atmosphere. A timber

wine rack at the entrance is well combined with the ceiling that leads to the bar, creating the continuity and integral effect in vision and adding the sense of depth in space. The wall adopts the Indian and Tai-style building patterns to echo with the mezzanine and forms the tropical relaxed ambience when opening the sliding grid window set off by the patterns. Each guest sitting here can experience the free and low-pressure environment as if they place themselves near the sea. The light ornaments achieve strong contrast against the dark timber, which makes the whole environment stable and bright.

There are a big chandelier and a drape from the void to the ceiling with their beautiful performance in this 6-meter-high space. As the breeze blows, the wavering drape gracefully dances and apparently brings in the sea breeze within the space. Owing to some treatments, the special structure of the top ceiling makes this originally inflexible space a peaceful place where bosom friends can chat and enjoy the food.

The entire space only uses some simple materials like wood, stone, voile and glass, which are sufficient to create an agreeable, bright and roomy environment.

1. Two square columns are the "bridges" linking the upper and lower space
2. The patterns and colors on the seating make this space close to nature
3. The decorative painting on the wall evokes the tropical leisure feeling in his environment
4. Glazed panels make the upper space more capacious

. 两根方形的立柱成为连接空间上下部的"桥梁"
. 坐椅的花纹与色调将空间与自然的距离拉得更近
. 墙面上的装饰画将热带的闲适情趣引入空间
. 玻璃的栏杆让楼上的空间更显轻巧

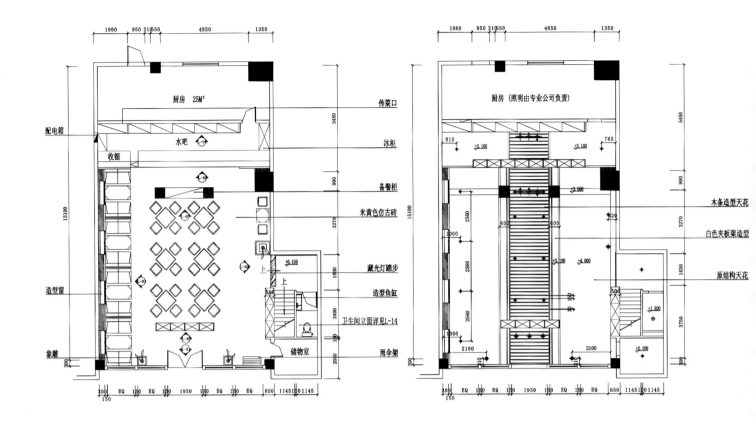

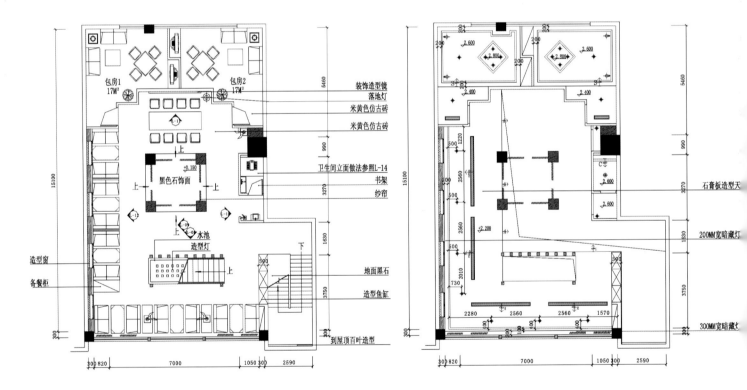

1. 2nd floor plan and plan of ceiling
2. 1st floor plan and plan of ceiling
3. This place shows the combination of softness and rigidness
4. The space under the staircase is designed as lotus pond, which is the most attractive ornament in this space
5. A curved glazed door is very inviting at the restaurant entrance

1．二层平面图、天花图
2．一层平面图、天花图
3．这一角落足以体现柔与刚的交融
4．楼梯下的空间被设计成一个荷花池，成为空间最生动的点缀
5．弧形的玻璃门使餐厅从入口开始就具有别样的风情

设计说明：

任何一个空间的设计都要考虑与周围环境的协调。素有"名闻天下，典藏原味"之称的名典咖啡语茶进驻万科城时，设计师就考虑到了这一点。万科城的建筑设计重在尊重基地的自然和人文环境，重视建筑与人、自然的亲和关系。一方面为了与这个整体建造风格统一协调，另一方面为了与我们印象中的咖啡西餐厅休闲、明亮的印象相符合，充分体现自然、和谐的主题，设计师打造了一个具有浓厚巴厘岛风情的个性餐饮空间。

本案以休闲式设计为主要概念，以明黄色与木色作主调，采用大量石材、木材等天然材料，把大自然元素融入设计之中。改造过的门头采用大块的玻璃，光线透过玻璃挥洒在室内，清新自然。入口的木质酒架与通向水吧的天花浑然连接，在视觉上产生一定的延续性，增加了空间的纵深感。墙面造型汲取印泰式建筑图案元素，与夹层相呼应，借用画面与木格推拉窗营造一种热带的闲逸情趣。让在座的每一位来客犹如置身海边，悠然自得。浅色的配饰与深色木质的强烈对比，让整个环境稳重而不失明亮。

中空至顶大吊灯与垂帘在六米高的空间中尽显其姿。清风拂过，摇曳的纱帘轻舞婆娑，似乎有一丝海风的味道在空间飘过。顶层天花的特殊结构在处理之后，使本不便利用的空间成为了供三五知己轻谈浅酌的宁静去处。

这个空间只运用了木、石、纱、玻璃几个简单的材质，却构架出一个令人心旷神怡、明亮通透的空间。

European Style

欧式风格

①.Bestcoffee，Tianyi
百世德咖啡天一店

②.Napoleon's French Brasserie
拿破仑法国餐厅

③.Xueke Coffee House
雪克咖啡厅

Perfection and Purity
极致纯粹

This space is full of energy. In this pure dining space, simple form embodies the more profound connotation.

空间是具有张力的，纯粹的餐饮空间，在简约的形式之中饱含更为深刻的本质内涵。

Title: Bestcoffee, Tianyi
Design company: Heaven Design
Designers: Wan Hongwei，Bao Mingda，Hu Dawei
Materials: OSB，Epoxy resin floor paint，Korean pine，Grey mirror，White emulsion varnish，White rostone
Floor area: 700m²

项目名称: 百世德咖啡天一店
设 计 师: 万宏伟、鲍明达、胡达维
设计公司: 汉文设计
主要饰材: 欧松板、环氧树脂地坪漆、红松、灰镜、白色乳胶漆、白色人造石
建筑面积: 700m²

	2
1	3

1. The compact between small compartment and the high space of lobby is partitioned by the windows
2. Neat surface treatment in the bar area
3. Sunshine in the afternoon obliquely filters through the window blending with pure and relaxed ambience

1．简约的小包厢与大厅被窗户隔开
2．吧区干净的界面处理
3．午后的阳光斜斜穿过百叶窗，纯净而闲适

1. The blue-grey mirror on the entire wall not only extends the in-depth of space but also makes a neat and clear spatial surface in the solid and void way
2. Wall details

1．整面墙面的蓝灰镜延展了空间的进深感，虚实空间界面干净利索
2．墙面的细节处理

Design Concept:

It needs a meticulous and exquisite process to make a cup of delicious coffee. Only after careful grinding and boiling can a perfect gustatory and spiritual enjoy be obtained. The design process of the cafe, quite the same as the making process of the coffee, needs elaborate conception and design to make the space become a kind of competitive product as the coffee does.

This case adopts the Nordic simple and splendid design style, and it uses the least and the most delicate design language to make the connotation of the space prominent, giving the feelings of simplicity and purity to people.

What impresses the designer first is the six high big windows on the second floor of the cafe. The big windows can make the special light more sufficient and strengthen the vigor of the space, which add purity and simple elegance to the space. Following the principle of simplicity, the designer recombines the space in the aspects of considering the interface processing, the material choice, combination, the command of details, the coordination of the lamp colors from the space, creating a pure room whose purity can enchant the people as the pureness of the coffee does.

Tasting slowly, purity is really a kind of state. Just like the lovers' eyes that can not allow the existence of any disadvantage, the pure perfection can not bear any impurities. Reduce again and again only to leave the most original essence, but to abandon all things that are flashy but without substance, and to leave the broadest space to imagination, thereby making the connotation much richer, ever-changing, succinct but not simple. It is the most important to discern the essence, to emphasize the details and to pursue the quality diligently.

1

1. The refinement of modern life comes from conciseness
1. 现代生活的精致来自简约

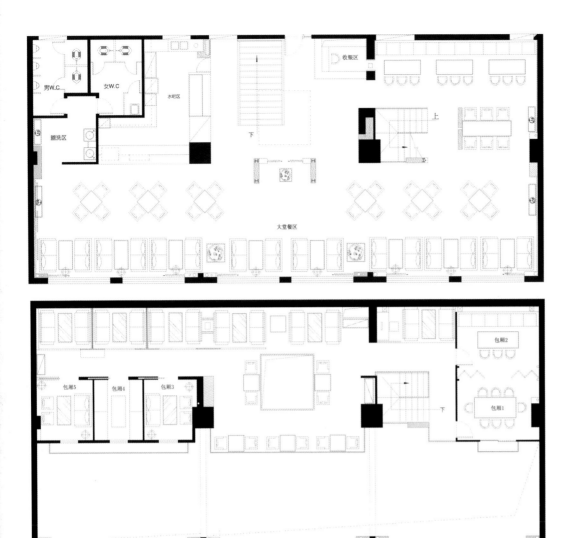

1. 3st and 4nd floor arrangement pla
2. 1st and 2nd floor arrangement pla
3. The spatial lines are very conci
and exquisite

1．三、四层平面布置图
2．一、二层平面布置图
3．空间的线条爽直而细腻

1. The door can partition the space when moving
2. The twinkling star-like droplights are the attractio
in the 2nd floor space
3. Decorative detail
4. Lamps

1．拉门隔断
2．如星星般璀璨的吊灯成为二楼空间的一道风景
3．装饰细节
4．灯饰组合

设计说明:

泡出一杯美味香醇的咖啡要经过一个细致、考究的过程。精心地研磨、烹煮，才能得到一次味觉和心灵的完美享受。咖啡厅的设计过程亦如同咖啡的制作过程，需要精心的构思、设计，让空间和泡好的咖啡一样成为一种精品。

本案例采用简洁大气的北欧设计风格，用最少、最精妙的设计语言突出空间内涵，给人简约、纯粹的感觉。

最初给设计师灵感的是咖啡厅二楼空间内六扇挑高的大窗，大窗能让空间的光线更为充足，亦能增强空间的活力，给空间一份纯净与淡定。本着简约的原则，设计师从空间体量界面的处理、材质的选择与组合、细节的分寸把握、灯光色彩的配合等方面将空间重组，搭建出一个纯粹的空间，空间的纯粹与咖啡的纯粹同样让人心醉。

慢慢品味，纯粹真是一种境界，就像情人眼里容不下一粒沙子，纯粹到极致也不容许一丝杂质，精简精简再精简，只留下最具创意的本体。抛弃一切华而不实的表象，把最广阔的空间留给想像，因而更显内涵的丰富，变幻无穷，简洁而不简单。洞悉本质、强调细节，执意着对品质的追求是最重要的。

1. The space only has the combination of materials without other decoration
2. Red roses in full blossom in this pure space constitute a classical picture
3. Tall curtain creates the charming space

1. 空间只有材质的组合，没有任何装饰
2. 红色玫瑰怒放在纯色空间里，如一幅经典的画卷
3. 长长的窗帘，是营造情调的高手

L eisure Space
暇逸空间

Leisure space atmosphere, artistic presentation and passionate heart.
This is a free catering space and also an environment to free your mind.
轻松的氛围、艺术的光芒、热情的心，这是个自由的餐饮空间，也是一个释放心灵的空间。

Title: Napoleon's French Brasserie
Designers: Ming Guanghua，Ming Gang
Design company: Shenzhen Xieyiju Architecture，
Decoration，Design and Engineering Co.
Materials: French membrane，Oil painting,
Ironwork，Mirror，Archaized brick，Wooden floor
Floor area: 910m²

项目名称：拿破仑法国餐厅
设 计 师：明光华、明罡
设计公司：深圳写意居建筑装饰设计工程公司
主要饰材：法国膜、油画彩绘、铁艺、镜面、仿古砖、实木地板
建筑面积：910m²

	2
1	3

1. Delicious food and sunshine
2. A big painting is enough to make the concise space full of cultural content
3. The restaurant entrance is surrounded by green plants

1．美食与阳光同在
2．大幅的油画足以让简洁装饰的空间充满人文气息
3．绿色植物簇拥的餐厅入口

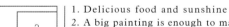

Design Concept:

Nepoleon's French Brasserie is a detached building known for its genuine French Brasserie cuisine. This is a romantic, comfortable and relaxed Western restaurant with French Brasserie features and the flavor of Corsica, which is Napoleon's hometown.

Being not a traditional restaurant, Brasserie is the product of fashion and new trend which the French people have pursued. It appeared at the beginning of the 20th century in France, and represents the popular restaurant style near the railway station. The strong artistic atmosphere is the most prominent feature of Brasserie. Elegant mural paintings and sculptures are employed to decorate many places of Brasserie, which make Brasserie an art gallery. As for the decoration of Brasserie, the most prevalent style of the 20th century is adopted here, including the roof full of artistic feeling, the refined wall decoration, and even the high back seat of the train. All of these create a distinctive catering environment. The cozy environment and the joyful ambience in Brasserie can effectively help clear up the differences and conflict between different groups. Brasserie is characterized by such a specific style, including casual clothes, compact

seats, lively atmosphere, delicious food as well as a place where bose friends can have a heart–to–heart and free talk at their will.

Corsica is a beautiful island in Mediterranean Sea. It has picturesc scenery, agreeable climate and sharp color contrast — blue sea, gre forest, brown city gate tower, yellowish brown wall, and red coast, wh are typical geographical features. As the tourism resort and Napoleo homeplace, it is also filled with the pronounced cultural context in addi to its beautiful views.

In this case, the design combines the features of French Brasserie with flavor of Corsica. When making use of the original building environm and the spatial advantages, the design adds a special staircase b tween the first and the second floor. There is a corridor under the lou that is set 6m on the second floor. A semicircle private room is placed in corridor, which not only avoids the higher ceiling of this small VIP room, also adds a quiet and comfortable dining space.

1	2

1. Two columns of unique shapes create the leisure and delightful ambience in the lobby
2. The bright spatial colors shape strong contrast against the clean and pure white tablecloth

1．造型独特的两个装饰柱让大厅具有休闲、愉悦的氛围
2．空间色彩的明丽与纯白桌布的洁净形成鲜明对比

e distribution of tables in exterior and interior spaces is easily change-
e and flexible, while the spatial arrangement is compact and neat. The
taurant ambience accordingly becomes much comfortable, relaxed
d lively.

e strong color contrast of Corsica is employed to create the Corsica-like
nosphere within this space. Wavy French membrane and gleamy ceiling,
al-shaped shining necking, painted column, golden rose-patterned
l decoration, crimson high back seat, brown archaized brick, exquisite
n craftwork, custom-made archaized lamp are used to match the well-
anged decorative oil painting, line drawing, stained glass, white
ecloth, glittering and translucent porcelain, silver plate and a number
flowers around. All of these jointly and thoroughly present the
aracteristic catering culture of this restaurant — the artistic French
sserie.

设计说明:

拿破仑法国餐厅是座独栋洋房,经营地道的法国自助餐厅风格菜肴。这是一个具有浪漫、舒适、轻松的法国"自助餐厅"特色和拿破仑家乡科西嘉风情的西餐厅。

"自助餐厅"并不是普通意义上的"餐厅",它是法兰西人追求时髦和新潮的产物,它起源于20世纪初的法国,代表了火车站旁人气旺盛的餐厅风格。具有浓郁的艺术气息是"自助餐厅"最重要的特色。大部分"自助餐厅"中都装饰着精美的壁画和雕塑,这就使自助餐厅都俨然成为一座艺术展览馆。"自助餐厅"在装潢上普遍采用20世纪最流行的模式,如艺术化的屋顶,精美的墙饰,甚至采用了火车上的高背车厢坐椅,营造出别样的风情。"自助餐厅"具有轻松舒适的环境和欢快热烈的气氛,能有效地调和不同人群之间的差别和对立。自助餐厅有着特定的风格——随意的装束、紧凑的坐椅、活跃的氛围、可口的美食,以及和亲密的朋友促膝共享的随心所欲,无拘无束。

科西嘉是座美丽的地中海小岛，风景秀丽，气候宜人，色彩对比强烈。湛蓝的大海，深绿色的森林，褐色的城楼，米色的围墙，红色的海岸是典型的特色地貌，作为旅游度假的胜地和拿破仑的出生地，在秀丽的风景之外又多了浓郁的人文气息。

设计师在空间内采用科西嘉强烈的色彩对比来营造科西嘉风情，将"自助餐厅"特色与科西嘉风情融合在一起。如发光法国膜的波浪造型天花、花瓣式发光法国膜柱头、彩绘圆柱，用餐区铺设了褐色的仿古地砖、精致的铁艺，又搭配了金色玫瑰墙饰、特制的仿古灯饰、装饰油画、素描、彩绘玻璃。雪白餐桌布、晶莹剔透蓝色瓷器、镀银餐具，加上餐厅内诸多鲜花点缀，将极具艺术性的法国"自助餐厅"文化淋漓尽致地展示出来。

设计师在充分发挥原有建筑环境和空间优势的同时，于一、二楼间增设了一架专用客梯，于层高达6米处的二楼天窗下架设了一条回廊，布置半圆形雅座，既避免小空间VIP房天花过高，又增加了幽静而舒适的进餐空间。

室内外餐桌布置既富于变化又便于流动，空间组织紧凑而轻松。餐厅氛围因而显得舒适、从容、欢快。

1. Nightscape
2. Photos and mirrors are pieced together to show a scene
3. The wall lamps and reading lamps add a touch of elegance in the leisure ambience
4. The wooden dining table and kerosene lamp are evocative of the unsophisticatedness and kindness of hometown

1．夜景
2．图片、镜面"拼凑"出的风景
3．壁灯和台灯为休闲氛围增加的几分优雅
4．室外的原木餐桌和煤油灯给人以家乡的淳朴与亲切感

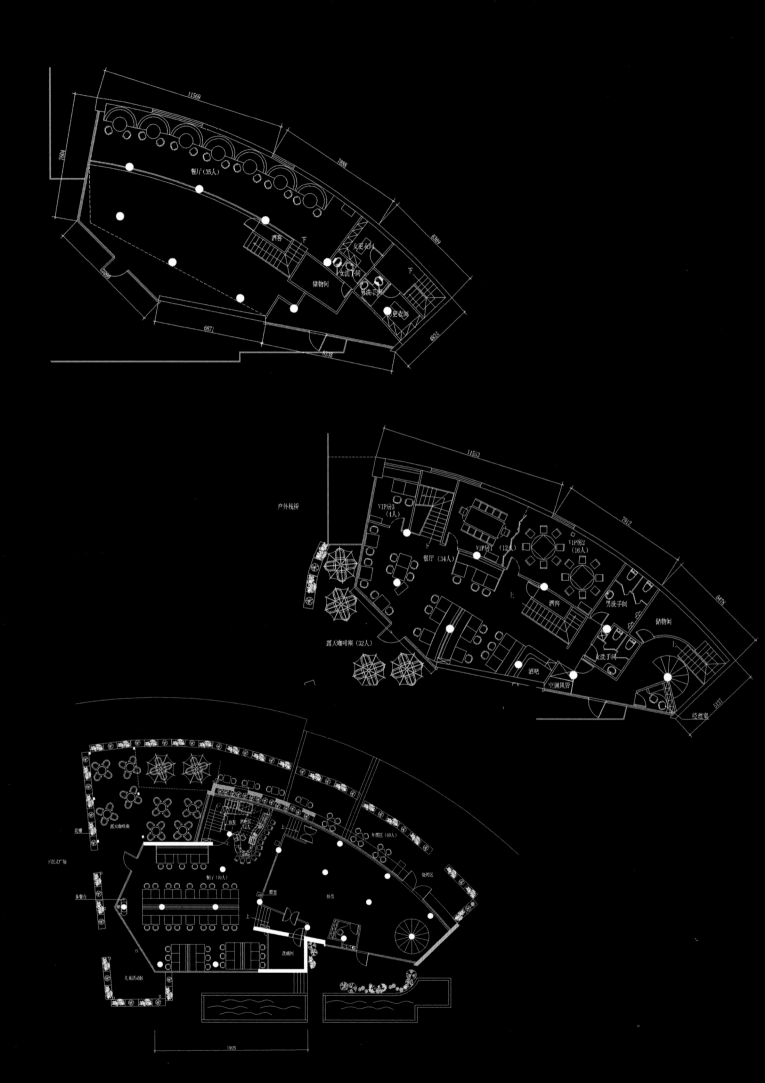

餐厅（35人）

酒客

下

女更衣间

储物间

女洗手间

男洗手间

下

更衣间

户外栈桥

VIP房3
(4人)

餐厅（34人）

VIP房1 (12人)

VIP房2
(16人)

酒客

男洗手间

储物间

露天咖啡座（32人）

女洗手间

酒吧

空调风管

经理室

露天咖啡座

下沉式广场

备餐台

餐厅（76人）

外摆区（60人）

吸烟区

厨房

洗碗间

儿童活动区

花槽

1\2\3. 3rd, 2nd and 1st floor arrangement plans
4. A bar near the stairway
1\2\3. 三、二、一层平面布置图
4 .位于楼梯旁的吧台

Coffee Hour
咖啡时光

Catering has become a culture with long-lasting history. Nowadays, more and more catering spaces are decorated by culture. They are not just the spaces but the symbols of certain history and culture.
餐饮文化有着悠久的历史，餐饮空间如今也越来越被文化"武装"起来，它们不仅是一个空间，而是某些历史、某种文化的象征。

Title: Xueke Coffee House
Designers: Fan Jiang，Lu Yi
Design Company: Ningbo Gaode Decoration and
Design Co.,Ltd.
Materials: Mosaic，Stone，Timber，Red brick
Floor area: 1,100m²

项目名称：雪克咖啡厅
设 计 师：范江、卢忆
设计公司：宁波市高得装饰设计有限公司
主要饰材：马赛克、石材、木材、红砖
建筑面积：*1100m²*

1. The straight wooden boards constitute the main shape of wall, casual but delicate
2. This capacious space makes people feel being outside
3. The scattered silver mirrors and brown mirrors here and there enable people to enjoy different places from different perspectives. This mini stage is the high spot of this coffee house

1．深浅相间的直木档是墙面的主要造型，随意却透着周密的心思
2．豁然开朗的空间，让人体会到户外的感觉
3．多处用到的银镜、茶镜使人在不同角度欣赏到不同的"风景"。小型的演歌台的布置是这个咖啡厅的一个特色

Design Concept:

The designer draws inspiration from the strange and irregular building that has bad exposure to sunshine and ventilation, and thus he designs this Xueke Coffee House. In order to create an exceptionally featured space, the designer deliberately sets a stage here. This is a stage for the soul of the busy people in the city. Music, unostentatiousness and kindness of the European ancient coffee house, leisure and low-pressure atmosphere together constitute the general profile of Xuke Coffee House.

Due to the higher spatial layers, the interior space is divided into interlaced levels and split level after rearranging the circulation. As the building within building, the mezzanine made up of red brick gives a sense of small house with the home warmth in the natural designs. Timber long tables, dark color timber doors and windows all remind people of the minute when Katharine Hepburn opens the window in a simple and unsophisticated inn in the film "Summertime". The sentiment of European bourgeois, together with the exquisite and delicate details without showiness is just like the refined coffee with fragrance. The original colorful steel plates are replaced by the glaze roof decorated by the wavy screens. The outdoor leisure furniture, bright light and the relaxed ambience all constitute a roadside coffee house in the sun, where people can experience two absolutely different flavors in a harmonious and integral environment. It is obvious that there is no bad to create a coffee house within the disordered building, and sometimes the designs can even work by making surprise techniques.

As the lines are concise but full of rich connotation, in the eyes of th designer, they are repeatedly used here. There are so many lines that the can compose a large number of shapes. The sense of line in this room extremely strong: custom-made mosaic flooring, stones in black and whi in the bar area, the light and dark battens on the wall, the bar in the silv mirror, dark ochre and wooden floor board and etc. In addition, there a the custom-made lampshades that is made by smaller lines, pleate blind, and the slots between red bricks··· These individualized designs only achieve a better effect in the appearance, but also enjoy favorak cost. The content of these designs is interpreted by the shapes and colo The table, desk and lighting are all custom-made in details, and the orna ments are also of originality. A black-and-white Paris old scenic pho bought in the old bookstore can just function as the wall background a decorative picture to glorify the walls.

In this unique coffee house, in the soft and subdued light, one can enj the light fragrance when listening to the blues of a Malaysia old man This place conjures up many stories about coffee. Just have a cup coffee and taste it slowly.

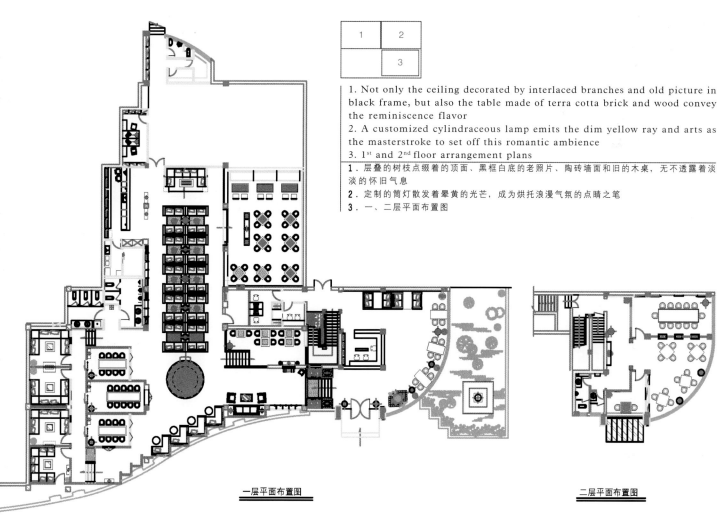

1. Not only the ceiling decorated by interlaced branches and old picture in black frame, but also the table made of terra cotta brick and wood convey the reminiscence flavor
2. A customized cylindraceous lamp emits the dim yellow ray and arts as the masterstroke to set off this romantic ambience
3. 1st and 2nd floor arrangement plans

1．层叠的树枝点缀着的顶面、黑框白底的老照片、陶砖墙面和旧的木桌，无不透露着淡淡的怀旧气息
2．定制的筒灯散发着晕黄的光芒，成为烘托浪漫气氛的点睛之笔
3．一、二层平面布置图

一层平面布置图

二层平面布置图

设计说明：

在不规则、采光不好、通风不良的建筑中捕捉灵感并进行创作是克咖啡厅的设计过程，设计师为了打造一个与众不同的空间，在里特别推出了一个演歌台。音乐氛围、欧洲旧时代咖啡店的质朴、亲切、悠然的低调闲情，都市里繁忙人们的心灵驿站，这些是雪咖啡厅的大致轮廓。

室内空间层高较高，因此被处理成错落有序的搭层、错层，包厢建筑中的建筑，用红砖搭建给人以小屋的感觉，自然中含有家的存。实木长桌、深色木百叶的门与窗让人想起凯瑟琳·赫本在《阳天》中那古朴的旅馆推窗的一瞬间，欧洲中产阶级不事张扬却究细节精致的情怀如咖啡般细腻，幽香致远。建筑原搭建部分的钢板顶被拆去，改为玻璃顶，配以波浪状的遮阳帘、户外休闲式具，充足的采光、轻松的格调让人想起沐浴在阳光下的路边咖啡厅顾客可在一个和谐统一的环境下品味两种不同的风情。可见，碰杂乱无章的建筑并不全是坏事，有时还能出奇制胜。

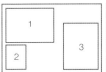

1. A lot of straight lines add the sense of order in this free space
2. When standing by the windows, people can see the ordered dining tables and chairs, which deliver a sense of warmth of European rural family
3. When opening the folding door, the compartment can directly link the lobby offering a stage for enjoying music; when closing the door, this space becomes a private environment

1．大量的直线条给杂乱的空间带来一些秩序感
2．站在窗前所看到的整齐排列的餐桌餐椅给人以欧式乡村家庭的温馨感
3．推开折叠式的木百叶门，使包厢与大厅互通，客人可欣赏演唱，合上则增添了空间的隐秘性

直线在这里得到反复的运用，在设计师眼里，直线是简约且感情丰富的，它可以变幻出无数的造型，取之不尽，用之不竭。这个空间的直线感非常强烈：定做的马赛克地坪、吧台黑白相间的石材、墙上深浅相间的木条、银镜中的木档、深赭石与木本色的条状地板等等，更细的线如定制的灯罩、百折帘、红砖与红砖之间的勾缝……这些个性化的设计不仅在美观上取得了好的效果，还在造价上占有优势。桌子、椅子、灯具都可以看出设计定做的痕迹，配饰也是独具匠心。如在旧书摊淘得的一册巴黎黑白风景老照片作为墙面背景和装饰画，让墙面变得风情万种。

别样的咖啡屋里，柔和淡定的灯光、马来西亚老人的蓝调歌曲、若隐若现的醇香……让人想起许多与咖啡有关的故事，真应该喝上一杯咖啡，细细品味一下咖啡的感觉。

1	3
	4
	5

. Wooden color, dark brown and yellow⋯The expression of coffee greets you
. The artless and simple red brick, wooden fork and gallipot bring in a sense of tranquility
. The customized mosaics of various colors are employed to pave the unique flooring; the furniture bought in other places is as old as the worn ornaments in our home and is very amiable
. Crystal and transparent tableware and these beautiful things dazzle people
. Log tables and chairs impress simplicity of European village to the space

. 木本色、深褐色、黄色……迎面而来的是咖啡的感觉
. 红砖墙、木叉、陶罐，它们的自然、质朴给人以宁静的享受
. 不同色彩的马赛克组合是定做的，铺设出如此独特的地面；选购的旧家具，陈旧如家中用了多年的物品，让人看着亲切
. 晶莹剔透、琳琅满目的酒水柜
. 原木桌椅摆设向空间传递着欧式乡村的淳朴

Other Styles

其他风格

①.Tianyu Hotel Dining Hall
天域大酒店餐厅

②.Parana Brazilian B.B.Q.
巴拉那烧烤餐厅

Neo-orientalism
新东方主义

Escaping from the chain of sheer space designing pattern, it approaches a special aura by blending and interlacing similar styles.

摒弃纯粹风格的空间设计模式，将相近的风格融合，使之相互穿插、掩映，孕育出独特的风味。

Title: Tianyu Hotel Dining Hall
Designer: Zou Zhixiong
Design company: Guangzhou Fangwei Decoration Co.,Ltd.
Materials: Imported botticino fiorito，Serpegg−iante，
Timber，Bamboo
Floor area: 1,200m²

项目名称: 天域大酒店餐厅
设 计 师: 邹志雄
设计公司: 广州方纬装饰有限公司
主要饰材: 进口米黄石材、木纹石、实木、毛竹
建筑面积: *1200m²*

1. Warm light
2. Hexagon buffet platform takes a grand appearance in the light of the ceiling
1．暖意灯光
2．六边形的自助餐台在顶部灯光的映衬下更显气派

1. Scenery in the open court
2. Open space with a cluster of green plants makes a more comfortable environment

1．敞亮的中庭美景
2．开阔的空间，簇拥的植株，让就餐有一个更为舒适的环境

Design Concept:

The interior design of Tianyu Hotel is in a style of Neo–orientalism which is highly internationalized and nationalized. The designer pours plenty of fashionable elements into this classic style, to make the space rich both in ancient and modern senses. Based on the overall style, it is persistent in its own style as well.

Consisting of two parts — western restaurant and Japanese restaurant, the former taking up an area of 630m². With glass wall at the corridor side which corresponds with the outside glass wall, the western dining hall looks modern and fashionable, forming a bright environment for dining. A hexagon buffet table together with the screen is the last touch on the layout, while the polished counter and bar integrate into the simple yet tasteful style perfectly. Furthermore, more oriental elements are melted into this western design by means of carved screen.

In the contrast, the Japanese dining hall bears a striking feature of oriental style — Japanese local culture. The designer manages to make best use of the wooden screen and partition aided by the marble columns, classic and modern. Among all the elements, malachite green marble columns are most impressive, fashionable and stable.

The technique "starting with water and ending with water" adds much aura to the entire layout — artificial waterfall set at the entrance and also at the exit leaving a unique impression on the customers. Japanese Zen rockery features a traditional and antique flavor.

A recreation clubhouse functions as a link between the two halls , the middle of which a huge wooden screen represents delicacy and magnificence .Water edge along with the embossment and artistic glass is quite a good example of mixing fashion with classic, connecting the interior to the exterior, in which process brightness and spaciousness are achieved.

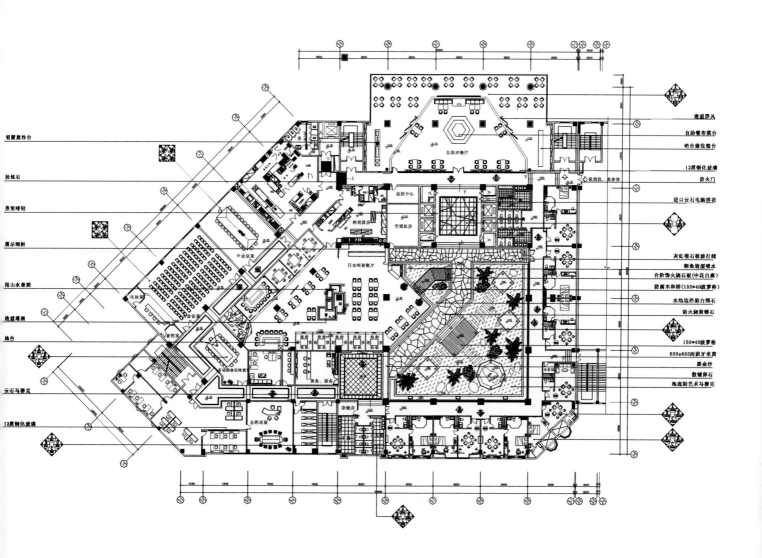

明厨煎炸台
拉丝石
皇室啤钻
展示酒柜
枯山水景观
造型墙座
地台
云石马赛克
12厘钢化玻璃

造型屏风
自助餐布菜台
吧台藏收银台
12厘钢化玻璃
防火门
进口云石电脑拼花

灰红根石板被打线
鲤鱼造型喷水
台阶饰火烧石板(中花白麻)
防腐木和桥(150*40萝格)
水池边栏贴白阀石
贴火烧黄锈石
150*40波萝格
600x600西班牙米贵
黑金沙
散铺卵石
池底贴艺术马赛克

1	3
2	4

1. Heavy aura of Zen vs simple Japanese style
2. A corner of the VIP room in Japanese style
3. Plan of the 3rd floor
4. Cozy and quiet atmosphere fills the VIP room

1．浓厚的禅宗气息让简约的日式空间韵味十足
2．日式风格的餐厅VIP房一角
3．三层平面布置图
4．日式设计的餐厅VIP房给人祥和、雅致的感受

| 1 | 3 |
| 2 | 4 |

1. With careful arrangement, relaxation is felt everywhere
2. Counter as partition is an eye-catching sight
3. Plan of pavement of the 3rd floor
4. Plan of ceiling on the 3rd floor

1．西餐厅的每一处布置都极为妥贴，令人感到心情舒畅
2．酒柜隔断是餐厅的一道风景
3．三层地平图
4．三层天花图

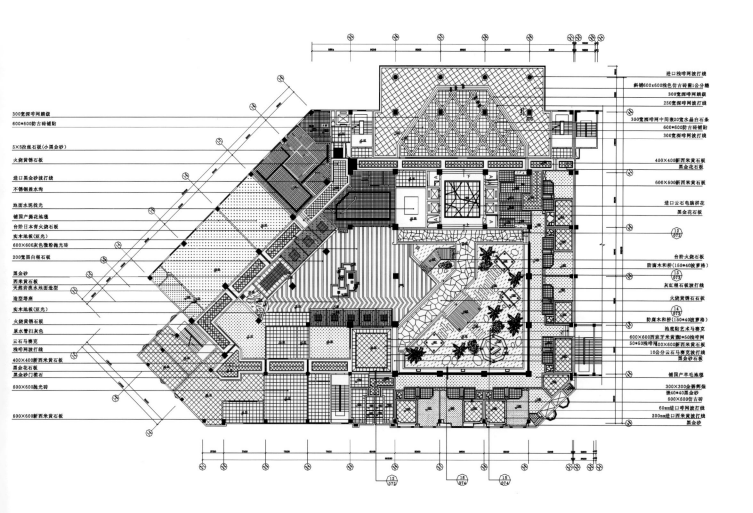

300宽深啤网踏磴
600×600防古砖铺贴
5×5拉丝石板(小黑金砂)
火烧黄锈石板
进口黑金砂波打线
不锈钢鱼鳞沟
地面水泥抹光
铺国产揉花地毯
台阶日本青火烧石板
实木地板(亚光)
600×600灰色微粉抛光砖
200宽黑白根石板
黑金砂
西米黄石板
天然岩溅水地面造型
造型塔座
实木地板(亚光)
原水磨扫灰色
云石马赛克
浅啤网波打线
400×400新西米黄石板
黑金花石板
黑金砂门槛石
600×600抛光砖
600×600新西米黄石板

进口揉啤网波打线
斜铺600×600浅色仿古砖前1公分槽
300宽深啤网跳磴
250深啤网波打线
300宽深啤网中间嵌20宽水晶白石条
600×600防古砖铺贴
300宽深啤网波打线
400×400新西米黄石板
黑金花石板
600×600新西米黄石板
进口云石电脑拼花
黑金花石板
台阶火烧石板
防腐木和桥(150×40波萝格)
灰红根石板波打线
火烧黄锈石板
防腐木和桥(150×40波萝格)
池底贴艺术马赛克
600×600西班牙米黄勘×50啤网
50×50揉啤网600×600新西米黄石板
10公分云石马赛克波打线
黑金砂石板
铺国产羊毛地毯
300×300金碧辉煌
嵌40×40黑金砂
600×600防古砖
60mm进口啤网波打线
200mm进口西米黄波打线
黑金砂

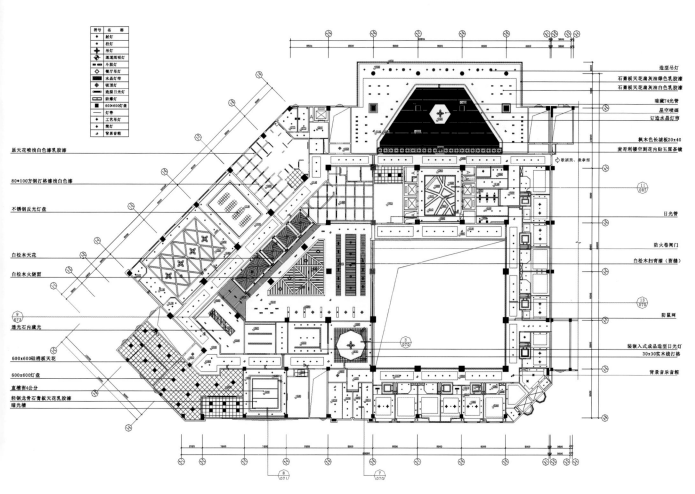

原天花喷浆浅白色漆乳胶漆
80*100方钢漆打格搭浅白色漆
不锈钢反光灯盘
白松木天花
白松木火烧面
透光石内藏光
600×600硅钙板天花
600×600灯盘
直槽面4公分
轻钢龙骨石膏板天花乳胶漆
暗光槽

造型吊灯
石膏板天花扇灰油绿色乳胶漆
石膏板天花扇灰油白色乳胶漆
暗藏T4光管
星空喷画
订造水晶灯带
枫木色长城板20x40
麦哥利镂空刻花内贴五厘茶镜
日光管
防火卷闸门
白松木扫背漆(面缝)
防鼠网
装嵌入式成品造型日光灯
30x30实木线打格
背景音乐音箱

设计说明:

天域大酒店的室内设计采用了新东方主义设计风格,这一风格具有高度的国际化、民族化特点。设计师在东方古典风格中注入了大量时尚元素,使空间古意浓厚又不失现代感。酒店餐厅在总体风格的定位下,仍保持有自己的特色。

本餐厅分为西餐厅和日本料理餐厅两个部分。时尚、现代的西餐厅占地630㎡,靠走廊一面全部用钢化玻璃做墙体造型,与对面外墙玻璃相呼应,营造出通透、明亮的用餐环境;六边形人造白沙石的自助餐台与拉丝屏风的相互映衬使餐厅的布局更加合理自然;餐厅两边酒水柜及吧台运用透光石打光,配合自助餐台的人造白沙石,统一、简约又不失品味;沙比利实木屏风镶嵌造型砂岩雕花更使其在风格上将传统的西式设计东方化,注入了更多东方文化元素与内涵。

而日本料理餐厅则更明显地突出东方特色和区域文化。设计师在570㎡的范围内运用大量木制屏风及隔断搭配大理石造型立柱,在古典的东方情调下融入现代时尚元素。日本料理餐厅的设计中尤为精彩的是的几根立柱,孔雀绿大理石搭配文化石的造型使整个餐饮空间沉稳不落俗套。

餐厅在整体布局上运用"成于水而止于水"的手法,在餐厅进口萝格造型桥)与出口处(人造瀑布)设计造型不同的水景使食客在餐前后都能感受到东方文化的不同韵味。再利用日式禅宗的枯山造将日式情韵蕴含其间,使空间透着一股古朴、传统的舒适气息。

连接日本料理餐厅和西餐厅的,是一个休闲会所,即三楼公共休闲的中庭,醒目的近9米长的实木屏风首先让人感到了餐厅设计的大细致,中庭无边界水景与墙面大型艺术砂岩浮雕、艺术压铸玻璃等现了时尚与古典的相互穿插、融合,贯穿的自然元素,室内与外境密切相连,给人以明朗、开阔、舒畅之感。

1	2
	3 4 5

1. Oriental element adds the charm of Japanese style to the dining hall
2. Japanese dining hall is designed with care and creativity
3. Massive use of timber is a characteristic of Japanese style
4. Wall paintings and droplights embrace a kind of heavy culture
5. The dining layout in the corner makes a compact space

1．日式风格的餐厅设计中加入了东方文化元素，让空间更具魅力
2．日本料理餐厅有着独具匠心的造景
3．大量运用原木是日式空间设计的一大特色
4．壁画和吊灯包含着浓厚的日本文化
5．餐厅一角靠墙的餐位布置让空间显得紧凑而恰到好处

1. Droplight brings in a touch of nature
2. The ceiling gives off a fresh smell of nature
3. Soft light builds a peaceful atmosphere for customers

1. 吊灯将一种朴质的自然气息带入餐厅
2. 天花设计具有清新的自然气息
3. 柔和的灯光给就餐者营造一种祥和的氛围

Four-dimension Space
四度空间

A complete space is expected to be omni bearing — including not only the basic forms of space but moreover, human senses like smelling, touching , hearing, seeing and space sense are essential.

一个完整的空间应该是全方位的，除了空间的基本形态外，还应具备人的感知：嗅觉、触觉、听觉、视觉及空间感应度。

Title: Parana Brazilian B.B.Q.
Designer: Qin Yueming
Design company: Shenzhen Langlian Design Consulting Co.,Ltd.
Materials: Stainless steel, Voile curtain
Floor area: 580m²

项目名称： 巴拉那烧烤餐厅
设 计 师： 秦岳明
设计公司： 深圳市朗联设计顾问有限公司
主要饰材： 不锈钢、纱幔
建筑面积： 580m²

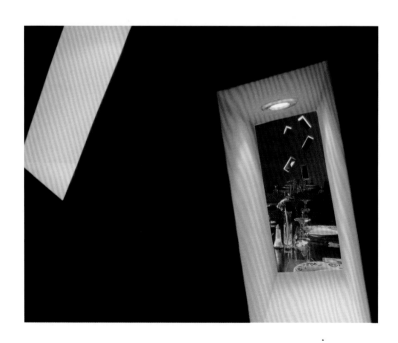

1. A special view comes in your way from this slanted perspective
2. The ship-shaped dining platform is significantly symbolized

1．倾斜的视角，给你一片独特的风景
2．船形的餐台是极具象征意义的一个设计

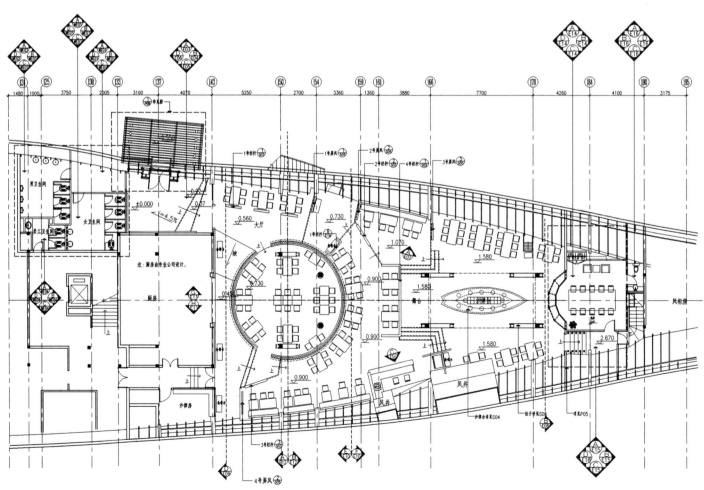

Design Concept:

Conception: This case is situated at "ANCEEVILL" in Sea World of Shekou, Shenzhen. It is hard to reform it for its low and narrow space which exerts much pressure on the reconstruction task. Along the slope of the cabinet, reasonable arrangement guaranteed, the designer extracts the "degree" conception, and also evolves it, designing it according to "degree". He controls the prosperous commercial atmosphere rationally, so as to limit it to a reasonable degree.

Space Elements: From the floor to the clapboard and to the ceiling, lines are basic elements in this case. From line to space, it brakes up the plane's balance, looking vivid and rich.

Color: This restaurant is featured with Brazilian Barbecue. The dominating color is originated from the national flag, the most characteristic one in Brazil. Assorting with linear space elements, it reaches an extended and enhanced visual effect.

Materials: The original material of the ship remains, assisted by soft and transparent yarn curtain, thus a sort of contrast comes into being, that is between tough and tender. The former can express itself by means of the latter: the stainless steel lamp is furnished with silk yarn which is swinging in the wind and glittering in the light. What a combination of beauty!

Four-dimension Space: A complete space endowed with human perception — extending from point to line then to surface, cascading from color to texture, it contains diverse elements through human recognition. Either sea foam or spray, passion or sweat, even only an abstract painting, a kind of mood, a sense of taste, they are inevitably attractive.

1			
2	3	4	

1. The dining location is in perfect coordination with the layout of the cabin
2. Arrangement plan
3. The irregular arrangement of cavities chiseled in the wall forms a kind of abstract art
4. A romantic aura is achieved by the use of yarn valence

1．餐位的布置与船舱的布局很协调
2．平面布置图
3．墙体凿出的方形洞无序排列成一种抽象艺术
4．纱幔围合出的情调空间

1. In this narrowness, slanted lines on the yarn vale
express a mixture of tenderness and toughness
2. The entrance of the restaurant takes on an appeara
of an abstract painting — consisting of lines and sha
of colors
3. Bright yellow effectively relieves the depression fr
this low space

1．狭窄的视线里，用纱幔编成的斜线展现了柔与刚的糅合
2．餐厅入口是线条与色彩构成的抽象画
3．明亮的黄色色调能有效地舒缓空间低矮给人的压抑感觉

计说明：

念: 本案位于深圳蛇口海上世界的"明华轮"内。低矮逼仄的内部空间给改造带来大压力。依据船舱的倾斜角度，在合理安排功能的前提下，设计师将"度"的概念以提炼与演变，依"度"行事。理性控制场所应具有的热闹的商业氛围，使其能达适度的范围。

间元素: 成一定角度的线是本案的基本元素，从地面延伸到墙面及天顶。由线到面，破平面的平衡，使空间具有张力，并与原有船体的倾斜面相呼应，从而建立一种新秩序与平衡，生动而丰富。

彩: 本餐厅为具有巴西风味的烧烤餐厅，在色彩上以巴西最具代表性的国旗色为基素材加以演化，配合线性的空间元素加以延伸及强化视觉效果。

料: 保留原有船体的金属件，辅以柔和透明的纱幔，产生刚与柔的对比。刚性的材料可达到柔性的感触：中心点的灯具以镜面不锈钢管为素材，截成小段再以丝线吊迎风摇摆，在灯光的照射下闪闪发光，刚与柔在此完美结合。

空间: 这是一个完整的空间，除空间的基本形态外，还具备着人的感知因素。由线及面的延伸，从色彩到元素及质感演变，其抽象的隐喻因人的解读而呈现丰富它可以是大海的泡沫与浪花；也可以是巴西人的激情与汗水；或者只是一幅印象抽象绘画；一种心情、一种味觉，或是更多的感知……

1	2

1. In order to divert people's attention from the tightness of the space, the designer attaches much emphasis on the details
2. The light in the wall exerts a strong sense of lines

1．设计师运用细节装饰吸引人的视线，让人忽略了空间的局促
2．墙内的灯光让空间的线条感很强

Designer Profile
设计师简介
(排名不分先后)

梁景泉
Liang Jingquan

1977年出生；
毕业于广州美术学院环境艺术设计专业；
2003年至今，任深圳名斯利烨家具·装饰设计有限公司设计总监；
CIID中国建筑学会室内设计分会会员；
IFDA国际室内装饰设计协会理事；
IFDA国际室内装饰设计协会资深会员；
曾获奖项：
2006年获海峡两岸四地室内设计大奖赛公共建筑工程A类一等奖；
2006年获中国（深圳）第二届室内设计文化节优秀室内设计银奖。

本书所选项目：
名典咖啡语茶（万科城分店）

范江
Fan Jiang

CIID中国建筑学会室内设计分会会员；
IFI国际室内建筑师／设计师联盟会员；
1999年创立宁波市高得装饰设计有限公司，现任总经理及设计总监；
作品多次刊登于《室内设计与装修》、《中国建筑装饰装修》、《美国室内》中文版、《现代装饰》等专业杂志，并在国内多次获奖。

本书所选项目：
雪克咖啡厅

刘杰
Liu jie

1985年毕业于天津工艺美院环艺系；
现任天津市建筑设计院副总建筑师、建筑装修所所高级建筑师；
曾获奖项及荣誉：
2005年获"全国百名优秀室内设计师"、"2005中优秀酒店设计师"荣誉称号；
2005年项目"丝竹坊酒吧"获第二届海峡两岸四地内设计大赛特等奖；
"透明的空间"项目获第一届"吉象e匠"中国住宅内设计大赛最佳奖。

本书所选项目：
和亭日本料理
福莱仕西餐厅

冯嘉云
Feng Jiayun

1987年毕业于无锡轻工业学院工业设计系；
毕业后就职于中外合资无锡华德装饰工程有限公司；
2003年至今于上瑞元筑设计制作有限公司任董事长及董事设计师；
曾获奖项：
无锡锦沧文华商务酒店项目获2005年中国室内设计大奖赛优秀奖。

本书所选项目：
泓历皇朝大酒店零点餐厅

刘卫军
Liu Weijun

国家高级室内建筑师；
IARI国际注册高级室内设计师；
IFDA国际室内装饰协会理事及资深会员；
CIID中国建筑学会室内设计分会全国理事；
IAID全国最具影响力中青年设计师；
深圳十大室内设计师；
深圳市品伊设计顾问有限公司创始人兼设计总监；
从事室内设计行业十年来，以多元化的设计风格，推崇创意与文化相融的情感空间所著称，被誉为"空间魔术师"。

本书所选项目：
东海花园鹤港料理店

何永明
He Yongming

1973年出生；
1998年毕业于华南师范大学，获学士学位；
2000年于广东雅风建筑装饰工程有限公司任设计总监；
2003年成立何永明设计师工作室，主要从事建筑和室内设计；
2005年成为中国室内设计师协会注册设计师；
作品多次发表于《现代装饰》、《建筑技术及设计》、《ID+C室内设计与装修》等杂志。

本书所选项目：
蕉叶咖喱屋餐厅
乐嘉快餐厅

明光华
Ming Guanghua

深圳写意居建筑装饰设计工程公司总工程师；
为从事室内设计20多年的资深专业人士，对室内设计有着丰富经验和独到认识；
专业特点：
创新能力强，精于超大空间的设计，善长组织协调，有丰富的投标和施工经验；
设计理念：
以最精炼的建筑语言为客户诠释其心中最美好的功能空间。

本书所选项目：
拿破仑法国餐厅

江天伦
Jiang Tianlun

高级室内建筑师；
中国百名优秀室内建筑师；
深圳经典装饰设计工程有限公司董事长兼设计总监；
深圳江天伦设计师事务所首席设计师；
IFI国际室内建筑师／设计师联盟会员；
CIID中国建筑学会室内设计分会会员；
CBDA中国建筑装饰协会专家库成员；
曾获奖项：
2004年CIID中国室内设计手绘表现图大赛金奖；
2005年《现代装饰》杂志年度传媒奖／年度优秀设计奖。

本书所选项目：
赣彩轩酒楼

钱万鹏
Qian Wanpeng

浙江宁波汉森建筑装饰设计工程公司设计总监；
浙江杭州碧源房产公司设计顾问；
CIID中国建筑学会室内设计分会会员；
曾获奖项
"第一届海峡两岸三地室内设计大奖赛"三等奖；
"中国室内设计大赛"办公工程类优秀奖；
"中国室内设计大赛"商业工程类优秀奖。

本书所选项目：
玉湖蝶主题餐厅

秦岳明
Qin Yueming

1990 年建筑学专业毕业；
1999 年组建朗联设计顾问有限公司并任设计总监；
国内首批高级室内建筑师；
全国百名优秀室内建筑师；
中国建筑学会室内设计分会理事；
从业十余年来，同时涉足建筑和室内设计，认为建筑和室内本身就是同一及相互影响的，设计的基本点都是处理人与空间的关系。设计推崇空间的处理及对文化和传统的尊重，强调自然人文，以人为本的设计理念。

本书所选项目：
"明华轮"柏宁酒吧
巴拉那烧烤餐厅

余青山
Yu Qingshan

香港著名室内设计师；
1955 年生于香港；
1979 年在香港创立山川设计事务所（NORMAN DESIGN）并任总设计师兼管理人；
在北京、上海等城市开有分公司；
有众多案例刊登在国内外知名杂志上，如《中国商业空间》、《新上海餐厅》、《家居主张》、《Life Style》等。

本书所选项目：
天地一家
冰火缘

宋国梁
Song Guoliang

IFI 国际室内建筑师 / 设计师联盟会员；
CIID 中国建筑学会室内设计分会会员；
中国百名优秀室内建筑师；
宁波红宝石装饰设计有限公司董事兼总设计师；
设计范畴涉及商业会馆、银行、酒店、娱乐；
曾获奖项：
2005 年获"IFI 首届国际室内设计大赛"、"CIID 中国室内设计大奖赛"佳作奖；
2006 年获 2006 "INTERIOR DESIGN CHINA" 酒店设计优秀奖。

书所选项目：
紫鲸湾时尚酒店
万家灯火大酒店

庄仙程
Zhuang Xiancheng

毕业于广州美术学院环境艺术专业；
2003 年创立广州市徐庄装饰设计有限公司，并任设计总监及执行总监至今；
同时致力于工装与家装两个方面，且均有不少优秀作品，如广州隧道公司办公楼、东莞金豪港式茶餐厅连锁店、惠州蓝波湾别墅、广州中怡城市花园会所等。

本书所选项目：
金本餐厅

万宏伟
Wan Hongwei

1991 年毕业于四川美术学院；
1992 年开始从事室内设计；
现任宁波市汉文设计工作室总经理、设计总监；
IFI 国际室内建筑师 / 设计师联盟会员；
CIID 中国建筑学会室内设计分会会员；
以"执意纯粹，比多更多，比少更少"为设计理念。

书所选项目：
百世德咖啡天一店
宁波醉美时尚餐厅

邹志雄
Zou Zhixiong

毕业于湖北经济管理大学工艺美术系；
国际注册资深室内设计师；
法国国立工艺学院（CNAM）清大远教在读硕士；
IDA 国际设计师协会秘书长；
广州方纬装饰有限公司总监、总设计师；
曾获荣誉及奖项：
首届（2004）海峡两岸三地生态家居创意大奖赛金奖
2006 中国第二届室内设计艺术观摩展"十大最具观摩展示作品奖"；
2006（IDA）国际室内设计大奖赛酒店类金奖；
中国 2006 室内设计"十大新锐人物"候选人。

本书所选项目：
天域大酒店餐厅

王寄明
Wang Jiming

1960 年出生；
室内设计师；
CIID 中国建筑学会室内设计分会会员；
1997 年创立宁波新世纪装饰设计有限公司，现任总经理兼设计总监；
从事室内设计多年。

书所选项目：
新世纪北仑商务吧

王锟
Wang Kun

1978 年生于江苏省南京；
1998 年毕业于苏州工艺美术职业技术学院；
1999 年在南京某大型装饰公司任职；
2000 年在深圳某设计公司任职；
2001 年成为自由设计师；
2004 年成立深圳艺鼎装饰设计有限公司。

书所选项目：
花泽轩